PIGS

Derek Woodhead
serving mainly in
due to a disability
wine making, classical music and traditional jazz.
A life-long conservationist, he enjoys the countryside, especially the Dales and Moors of Yorkshire,
where he once served as a member of a police
rescue team. He now lives with his wife and two
daughters in their small house in the Dales, surrounded by cats, rabbits, guinea pigs and a dog –
all of which feature in his stories.

DEREK WOODHEAD

Pigs Might Fly!

Fontana/Collins

First published in 1988 by Fontana Paperbacks,
8 Grafton Street, London W1X 3LA

Printed and bound in Great Britain by
William Collins Sons & Co. Ltd, Glasgow

Contents

To Dad,
who would have loved all this

Author's Note

'PIG!'

The word was, at one time, guaranteed to make my hackles rise right up my back, especially when it was shouted at me from a distance by a callow and spotty youth who a few moments previously had stared fixedly into a window or doorway as I passed on my beat. Hardly a complimentary term, it is sad to see it has passed into English usage as; 'Pig. (sl.) derog. A Policeman.' (O.E.D.)

As I researched this book, I began to take more interest in the word. Strange to relate, I found that colleagues in the various forces were beginning to accept the insult almost as a term of endearment. Indeed, the animal counterpart was regarded with affection, even to the extent of a small badge being produced to wear as a tie pin.

With this attitude in mind, I determined to put across the message that the word has lost its insulting stigma. How better than to make the title of my book one which incorporated the word 'pig' as totally acceptable, like 'copper', or 'rozzer'.

Indeed, when one studies the pig in its animal form, close similarities to members of the police force emerge. For instance: 'A pig is a gregarious animal, clean in its habits. It is most adaptable in either a rural or urban situation, spending most of its time clearing up the rubbish that others don't want or wish to ignore. It has a penchant for investigating different aspects of its surroundings, poking its nose into seemingly innocent façades and bringing to the surface titbits of interest. It defends its own territory, (or beat) against others who would infringe on it in any way, yet it maintains a strong discipline within its own herd towards those who step out of line. Above all it has a thick skin!'

I had originally written this book under the title of *Plod On*. My editor, however, wanted something which would distinguish my book from the thousands of others lining the shelves.

Like most authors, I had written the manuscript with a single title in mind, and could in no way shake myself away from it. Not until I was strolling down New Bond Street on my way to a meeting. The deadline was fast approaching, and still the new title eluded me. Then I chanced upon a demonstration taking place, something to do with a left-wing march, and stood a while to watch, purely out of professional interest. There were young policemen and women in a cordon, holding back a crowd which was apparently incensed because it was unable to continue down a crowded and busy London street. Above the general mayhem, the word 'PIGS' was heard frequently from the intense and equally young members of the demonstration. A man standing next to me shook his head.

'They all need a taste of the birch!' he stated emphatically to his colleague alongside him. 'Bit of discipline needed there. This Government's got to bring back corporal punishment and hanging!'

His friend laughed ruefully, 'Ha! And pigs might fly!'

At this point, the Metropolitan Police helicopter throbbed and 'chop-chopped' its way overhead, monitoring the situation below. We all peered up at it, and from the crowd a fist punched into the air towards the aircraft, accompanied by the word 'PIGS!'

The humour of the statement by the demonstrator

and that of the slightly caustic gentleman alongside me regarding the Government's apparent inability to tighten up, made me laugh out loud.

'Pigs might fly', he had stated disbelievingly, and yet, up there above us, they did!

1

Early Days

I joined the police force after an inauspicious period in the RAF and, after demob, an equally inauspicious period working for BAC at Filton and Fairford on the Concorde project. In the former, I saw a lot of the world and in the latter I came into contact for the first and only time with trade unions. The world was large, invariably disappointing, and seemed to be totally incapable of providing a decent cup of tea anywhere except in England, Scotland or Wales. The unions and I made a mutual parting of the ways after I banjoed two shop steward 'heavies' in the toilets after they tried to lean on me to hold up my hand in favour of an overtime ban and work to rule that I did not think was necessary. Matter of principles, you see.

So, I decided to become a copper. It was one job where I knew the unions did not exist. On reflection, I am now of the opinion that it is the one job where a proper union is needed in a lot of cases, but that, I stress to point out, is my opinion!

However, I digress.

I finally ended up joining a rural force, and was sent to a Home Office training establishment after being 'sworn in'.

Funny old places, training establishments. When you arrive, you are conscious of the fact that you are the only person in about 7,000 who is in civilian clothing, and despite the fact that you are yourself a 'new' PC you still retain the natural reticence we all have to the police uniform and policemen in general. This means you are immediately nervous!

The general idea at Police Training College is to strip you of any ordinary identity you may have, and replace it with an attitude which makes you suspicious of everything and everybody. It is something which never leaves you, ever! Try walking into a crowded pub sometime with an off-duty copper and watch him. Eyes scan the people assembled, mental note made of the time, the ages of the drinkers, the drunk who is obviously going home with a car, a face which is similar to that currently being described in the *Gazette*. Ask any copper's wife what her husband is like when they go out for a meal. She'll tell you that he's twigged the local villains before the soup has been warmed and served! Not just that, he's also only half paying attention to her during the whole meal because he's also listening to the two youths talking quietly on the next table down.

The next thing the PTC does, is to try and get you and your syndicate into some semblance of fitness, combined with a general ability to march and think in a disciplined manner. Now, as an ex-serviceman, I did not think I was going to have too much trouble with either, but there are times when my thinking has led me to be totally wrong.

The drill instructors are invariably ex-guardsmen, and their identity is shrouded for the duration of training under a peaked hat which totally hides their features from the mouth upwards. Their language is about par for the average DI, but unlike their counterparts in the services, they are using it to a squad of people who comprise of both men and women. I can remember with clarity our DI who, on the first morning of drill, shouted at the top of his voice from a distance of a few feet at a

14

new WPC in the squad. She, in her ignorance of matters military, had omitted to polish her shoes and press her uniform properly.

'YOU F . . . SCRUFFY LITTLE SOD. WHO DO YOU THINK YOU ARE? DADDY LAID OFF THE F . . . BUTLER AGAIN DID HE? WHAT'S YOUR NAME THEN, LADY F . . . DOCKER IS IT?'

'No, it's Janine.'

'YOU F . . . WHAT?' eyes aghast and face apoplectic, chin now some two inches from the ashen-faced girl, 'YOU'RE ON F . . . MANK (extra duties). YOU'LL NEVER MAKE A POLICEMAN WHILE YOU'VE GOT A HOLE IN YOUR ARSE. WHAT ARE YOU LAUGHING AT?' This latter was addressed to me as I was grinning broadly. 'WELL?!! WHAT'S SO F . . . FUNNY THEN? GIVE US ALL A LAUGH, THEN. C'MON OFFICER, MAKE ME LAUGH. 'COS IF YOU DON'T I'M MAKING YOU MY PERSONAL VENDETTA.'

'I was just thinking that in this young lady's case, Sar'nt, she has got two things against her becoming a policeman.' Squad erupts into tight-lipped, tooth-gripping, shoulder-heaving sniggers whilst attempting to keep a straight face.

Chin then confronts me from two inches, and I detect a glimpse of eyes and nose under the slashed peak of his cap.

'WHAT'S THAT SUPPOSED TO MEAN? FUNNY IS IT? FUNNY?' – this to the lad next to me.

'Er, no Sar'nt,' this statement made mainly through diligent use of the nostrils, the bottom teeth dug grimly into the upper lip.

Beside me, the young lady PC was trying desperately to stop herself dissolving into a flood of tears. Lips trembling, blinking furiously over rapidly watering eyes, she stood with her hands clenched tightly by her sides.

'DON'T YOU BAWL ON MY SQUARE. IF YOU

15

WANT TO BLUBBER, THEN TAKE YOURSELF OFF TO THE CO AND RESIGN. I TELL YOU THIS, MY GIRL, YOU'LL HEAR FAR WORSE F . . . LANGUAGE THAN THIS WHEN, OR IN YOUR CASE, IF, YOU GET OUT ON THE STREETS. RIGHT?' Ashen-face nods in miserable assent. 'RIGHT THEN. SQUAAAD! SHUN!'

In truth, I have never heard language like it used either to myself or my female colleagues in any situation since I graduated. Anyone using a fraction of that amount of bad language was either warned or arrested. The young lady in question is now a respectably married wife and mother in Northumbria, but should she read this, I would point out that I made my comments about her female gender purely out of chivalry in an attempt to steer the brunt of the abuse away from her.

The fitness side of training was devoted in the main to getting as many people in the syndicate as possible to be able to run six miles over country terrain, complete and pass a Bronze medallion life-saving exam, play as many sports as possible for the centre, be able to do six circuits of the gymnasium training course without passing out, and defend themselves against fists, bottles, knives and guns with their bare hands. That included the girls as well. And this was before the sex equality act was passed. Very little deference was given to those girls unfortunate to be 'indisposed' during these lessons. They had to hope that one of the syndicate had remembered enough to teach them the rudiments of the self-defence during 'off duty' time. Those girls, all of them, had to work damn hard to complete the course. The PTI was a short, stocky man, just on the height minimum for a PC which in most forces was five foot nine inches. His forte was aikido; he was forever weight training to improve what to me seemed a supreme body, and he could swim like a fish. I hated him! He found out I could do karate, and was a higher grade than he was, and from that moment I was thrown, twisted, bounced and wrenched from every angle. It did wonders for my breakfalls, but nothing for my opinion of him. As an instructor, he was brilliant, because through him I learned to hold my temper, which is fiery by nature. I met him later in my career, and we found we could enjoy each other's company without animosity. I still regard him as a friend.

Once we were in the peak of fitness, then the book learning began in earnest. Now, I am not the world's best student, having a complete inability to readily commit to memory anything which I find either boring or, to my mind, totally irrelevant to everyday life. So it was with Law. The idea was that you memorized startling pieces of literature – such as definitions. Now definitions are the foundation stones on which you will build your police career. I mention this because I am still a PC which gives some indication as to how well my memory served me during those desperate early days! My old instructor would, on reading this chapter, no doubt nod sagely and agree with every comment I make against myself. I was useless! Even now, I stumble over the definition of 'A Constable', and I'm supposed to be one! He was a big man, of patience and dedication which must have been sorely tried throughout my thirteen weeks with him. A dry sense of humour combined with a love of classical music was the thing which he and I shared and which made life slightly more tolerable for both of us.

The theoretical side of the teaching was combined with the practical, which meant that in the latter the instructors could get their own back on the smart arses or dullards in their group. As I fell into both categories, I learned far more on the practicals than I ever did in the theoretical!

'Woodhead! Go round that corner in a few minutes. You will be confronted with an incident which could arise at any time outside. Deal with it to the best of your ability.'

'Yes Sar'nt.' Think quickly over the whole range of law we have been studying in the last few days. It must be something to do with liquor licensing. A drunk? Don't forget the caution.

One of our policewomen comes running round the corner and waves to me. Striding purposefully down the road in what I hope is an attitude of supreme confidence, I am confronted by the Sergeant, dressed in a civvy jacket, leaning on the door of his civilian car. In front of the car there is a cardboard box. The whole scene is surrounded by grinning policemen and women, notebooks out, pens poised and each revelling in the fact that they aren't the poor bugger who's going to cock up the whole thing!

I assess the situation.

'Right, what's happened here, then?' I ask one of the grinning group. No answer.

'You are supposed to assess the situation immediately, Woodhead. These people do not exist.' The sarcasm is heavy from another instructor.

At this point, my own sergeant begins to sing 'Nellie Dene' in a false contralto and falls about around his car with legs made of rubber. I was right! He's a drunk. I approach in determined manner, and slowly quoting the caution to him, place him in a Home Office approved arm lock and begin to march him, struggling and protesting his innocence to the now hysterical crowd, away from the scene.

'WHAT THE F . . . DO YOU THINK YOU'RE DOING, WOODHEAD?' The other instructor is holding his hand to his forehead.

'Er, I'm arresting him for being drunk and disorderly, Sar'nt.' Am I not right? Doubt begins to set in.

'DRUNK AND DISORDERLY. WHAT ABOUT THE PIG?!'

What sodding pig? I look in panic around the square, only aware that my 'friends' are convulsed with laughter.

'WHAT F . . . ING PIG? THAT F . . . ING PIG, THAT'S WHAT,' pointing to the squashed cardboard box under the front of the Cortina. Towing my prisoner with me, I look in surprise and horror at the crushed remains of what was once a large cardboard pig. The bloody thing didn't even have a snout! Just a hole and two eyes. I can feel my mouth opening and closing with no words coming out.

'You have supposedly attended an RTA which has involved a PIG. That is an animal as defined by the Road Traffic Act. The driver is in a state of shock, he is also subject to epilepsy and diabetes, his tax disc is out of date, and YOU HAVE LOCKED HIM UP FOR DRUNK AND DISORDERLY?'

At this point, my prisoner goes limp, falls out of my Home Office approved arm hold and drops twitching and slavering on the floor. I stand, to the delighted anticipation of my fellow students, mouth opening and closing whilst my instructor gives a brilliant interpretation of a centipede, and with a death rattle, expires in front of me. It gains him a round of applause from the syndicate, but I am still gob struck.

'Well, you messed that one up good and proper, Woodhead.' The other instructor is well pleased with my efforts. We learned from incidents like that. Mind you, I've never had cause to deal with an epileptic diabetic who has run over a cardboard pig since, but if I do, I'll know exactly how to deal with it.

We were examined on our learning ability with weekly examinations of the type classed as 'multiple choice', which gave the clever student the correct answer and the rest of us a one in four chance of getting it right. This random stabbing of my pen at a, b, c, or d enabled me, much to my instructor's amazement, to get pass marks in excess of the required 60 per cent.

Coupled with the weekly spelling tests these marks were placed on record to be assessed for the overall mark at the end-of-training examination. My results at the end of my training were such that I passed out halfway up the list, in the 'Average, likely to succeed as a Constable' category. Sergeant D's final words to me were, 'Good luck, Chip. I just pray that you don't end up anywhere near where I live!'

Funnily enough, my second posting had me as his local bobby, and I remember even now the glow of pleasure that I felt when I met him outside his bungalow with his son, and after the initial chat, he turned to his son who was staring at me and said, 'Don't stare, son, anyone would think you hadn't seen a proper policeman before.'

Praise indeed.

But even at the end of our stint at PTC, the threat of being asked to resign never left. One incident brought this home to me most forcefully on our last but one day, and also opened my eyes to a certain type of senior officer which was, and to some extent still is, prevalent in the police force today.

We marched on to the parade square every morning at 8.30 to the stirring strains of *Blaze Away* or something equally martial, to form up in our syndicates in blocks of seniority. There we were inspected and marched off past a saluting base under the gaze of a senior officer of Inspector or higher rank. Once a month we were inspected by the Commandant.

On this particular morning, it being our last parade before Passing Out, we, that is my syndicate, decided to liven up the proceedings with a touch of what we thought was humour. One of the lads dressed up as a policewoman, complete with wig and patent leather high-heeled shoes, and the front three, myself and two other ex-servicemen who should, on reflection, have known better, as the three American Revolution stooges. One with side drum and bloodied bandage round the head, one with his leg tucked up behind him and using a crutch whilst sporting a clay pipe in his mouth, and myself, led on with blindfold round the eyes in a tattered uniform playing a tin whistle.

To the thunderous strains of the *Colonel Bogey March*, we limped, crutched and groped our way down to the parade square, to the delight of the assembled ranks and with the approval of the DI, who at this stage of our training had, we found, developed a lovely sense of humour.

Forming up, we were inspected by the duty inspector (no pun intended), and were all three duly placed under arrest for impersonating human beings on parade.

The whole affair was one of light-hearted relief, and good-humoured camaraderie from all ranks assembled. Three junior syndicate members escorted us off the parade ground, and the instructors watching from the windows of the main building were laughing and clapping. Everybody, it seemed, had taken the whole affair in the manner in which it was intended. Except for one man. A very senior officer, who had seen the whole procedure.

Suddenly, all faces were grim. We four were ordered to get changed into proper uniform and be at the VSO's office in twenty minutes. Duly arriving, we were ordered in, and wordlessly handed a sheet of paper over the plush desk. Picking mine up, I saw it was a letter of resignation, just awaiting my signature. A look at my colleagues' faces showed theirs to be of similar vein. I refused to sign. A matter of principle. The Home Office had spent about £7,000 on my training, and that was in *old* money, when the pound was worth something, and there I was being ordered, by a man I would be most unlikely ever to see again in a full career, to resign and throw it all down the drain.

We were asked if we thought it funny, ruining a

21

parade. I said yes, I thought it had injected a little humour into the morning, and had apparently been enjoyed by everyone concerned. We were finally ordered out of the office with a flea in our ear, and the threat that the whole disgraceful display would be reported to our respective Chief Constables. I have met a few more like him over the years, and can honestly state that they all seemed to come from the same humourless mould.

Needless to say, my Chief Constable glossed over the whole thing in a light-hearted manner, saying that humour was an essential part of a constable's make-up. A great pity the incident was blown out of all proportion, because it put a damper on the whole course, and was something that even to this day makes me sad. A stand-up rollicking in front of the whole parade would have squashed any future antics and yet maintained the respect I felt I should have had for that humourless man.

2

A Matter of Communication

It has now become too expensive to dole out postings willy-nilly, unlike the old days when an officer could only expect to remain in one area for two years at the most. So for a Probationer Constable, the first posting was always at your own expense and usually to some place you either didn't want or never heard of. However, it was a posting that you knew would keep you in one place for at least two years if you lasted the pace.

A Probationer is an officer who is on just that – probation. I always regarded the title as being inappropriate to the office held. I mean, there you are, to all intents and purposes a police officer, and you're on probation before you start! It does mean though, that at any time in your first two years, the force concerned can dispense with your services as 'not likely to become a police officer' at the drop of a hat. Admittedly you have to be a complete wally to have such a decision made against you, but I have known it to happen. So, as a young copper, you are told that you must submit a wide and varied selection of work to keep the boss happy with your progress. Now the law is filled with a vast range of subjects which can be utilized against the unsuspecting public, some so obscure they go back eons and have never been rescinded or updated. And that doesn't include the by-laws, either. Armed with this fantastic arsenal, the young copper goes to his first station ready to do battle against all and sundry.

I arrived at my first station, a little apprehensive and with not a lot of confidence in dealing with 'the streets'. I was checked out on 'run over cardboard pigs', and in the latter stages of training, the last month in fact, on how to deal with a complete murder enquiry. The former, I knew, was unlikely. The latter, I prayed, wouldn't happen on my first day.

Don't laugh, though. A mate of mine was walking to work on his first day when he turned a corner in time to see someone get knifed. He coped, but how the hell he did I cannot imagine. The funny thing was, as he recalled later to me, he can distinctly remember running to the injured party, doing first aid and shouting to the onlookers to get on the phone and 'get a policeman'!

I'm reminded of my first shift sergeant, who impressed on me to 'get out there lad, and put pen to paper. The longer you leave it, the harder it is to get your first offence.' Bearing this in mind, I stood in the foyer of the station, looking vacantly around as members of the public came and went, when the same sergeant came over and put a kindly arm about my shoulders, directing me towards a quiet niche.

'Why are you still in the station, lad, when you are ten minutes into your shift?'

'I'm waiting for my tutor constable, Sar'nt.'

'Well, you're going to wait a long time, lad. You haven't got one. In fact, you're *it*. Now get out there and look busy.'

Bearing in mind I had only been posted the previous day, it was with great trepidation that I walked down from the 'nick' to the town centre, painfully aware that I was the only bobby in the streets, it was holiday time, I didn't have a clue where anything was, and it was most unlikely that I would be able to find my way back to the nick for my meal break! I think the last part worried me the most. I called at a tobacconist's shop and was given a sheaf of street maps, ostensibly to hand out to members of the public who were lost, and as I stood at the shop doorway, saw my first 'offence'. Driving in a one-way street in a direction other than specified. Gottim! Straight up and downer!

I pulled the driver in, cautioned him, pointed out the offence, held up my hand to quell his flow of protestation about it only being his second day in the town (dammit, he had more experience of the town than I did, so he should have known better), dutifully ignored his wife's blazing eyes boring at me from the passenger seat, and reported him. I then remembered I didn't know his name, address or occupation. With tight-lipped mono-tone he supplied the information I required, and I didn't realize my gaffe until I was writing down his occupation. Bradford City Police, rank: Chief Inspector. My hand shook. I decided against a lecture on keeping his eyes open in future, and on the need for careful driving in these days of hectic motoring! I saluted and waved him on. Principle again, you see?

The shift went over without any major incidents, mainly, I think, because I had omitted to take out a personal radio! I waited at the duly appointed 'points', which seemed to somehow destroy the whole principle of being in constant radio contact, but nothing was forthcoming. You made your point, I was informed, five minutes before and remained there until five minutes after the allotted time. The phone did ring at one box, and in a flurry of excitement and fear, I answered it in what I believed to be a real policeman's voice. The person on the other end enquired if 'Haggy' was there, and on being informed that it was a police officer and could I help, requested that I keep an eye out for a young woman dressed in green shorts who spoke with a Scots accent and, if I saw her, could I tell her that 'Bronco' couldn't make it. If 'Haggy' is reading this book, I'm sorry love, I must have missed you.

We were supposed to be with a tutor constable for six

weeks at the start of our probation, he being a senior bobby who took you under his wing and taught you all that was to be known about policing. I never got one. On reflection, and hearing some of the horrendous stories put about by my colleagues about theirs, perhaps it was a good thing too. They tended to be men who had joined at the end of the last war, and were very set in their ways. Never moved quickly to anything, especially a fight. Never put pen to paper if you could 'cuff it', that's 'write it off' to the layman, usually with either a verbal caution or a belt round the ear. They were men of stature in the community, always called 'Mister', and greatly respected by citizens and thieves alike. Yobboes were clipped on the ear, drunks were taken home to their wives and left to face the music, and they could get a 'cough' from the thieves usually before they had walked them halfway to the station. Great lads, but usually doing the job in their own way which was not quite what was expected from a probationer. They knew every skive, cup of tea spot, warm doorway and, in some cases, every 'watering hole' in their beat.

'Just stay here lad, whilst I pop up this alley and check the back of this pub,' to emerge some ten minutes later wiping their mouths with hairy backs of hands and smelling distinctly of something alcohol-based other than after-shave. They also had an uncanny way of knowing *exactly* where the duty sergeant was at any one time. Not that they were lazy. Far from it. If you ignored their little 'quirks', like being drunk at four-thirty in the morning after 'just checking the back of this pub, lad' business, a young officer could end up really knowing how to work a beat. And if your 'tutor' told the boss that 'the lad's alright,' it was taken as read. I never managed to get one like that! No, I stumbled through my first years in the force, blundering from one crisis to another.

As I said earlier in this chapter, the young bobby

went out on the streets with a bewildering amount of enforceable laws at his fingertips. One little incident which sticks firmly in my mind was when I had occasion to speak with a man who subsequently turned out to be a solicitor. He had parked his car such that I regarded it as being an obstruction. His attitude was very superior, and his knowledge of the Road Traffic Act was phenomenal. I realized early in the conversation that I was on to a loser at the best, and a complaint against police at the worst. I was just about to back off due to lack of basics (see Training School), with my tail between my legs, when I espied his large dog squatting down on the pavement, every muscle rigid in the hindquarters and a look of soporific contentment on its face as the 'world dropped out of his bottom'. Frantically trying to pull the still straining hound into his car, a wild-eyed look of panic on his face, the solicitor watched as the complete contents of a tin of Chappie were deposited in digested form on to the paving stones of a county highway. I took great pleasure in nicking him on a local by-law for allowing his dog to foul the footpath! Now *that's* justice!

I realized that in the police force one had to be correct and act without bias, but in that case, I readily admit to thoroughly enjoying the outcome!

I also realized very early in my career, that one senior officer's interpretation of force orders is not necessarily that of another. Now why this should be I do not know, but my word, it has caused some upsets in the job. Like making a 'point' when you have a personal radio. I can remember a great character in my first year. He was an inspector and one of the old school. Points to be made as stated in orders. Officers would not be seen in pairs, talking! I recall one evening when I was pounding the beat and heard the radio squawking my number. I answered, and heard the inspector ask in a loud voice whether I was at my point yet. On my giving a 'negative', he then bellowed that I was late, and that he was trying to contact me! By telephone! And he had to tell me over the radio!! Where have those characters gone?

I followed this inspector once, as he made his way home from a pub in the town. He entered a railway yard, after a good evening's drinking, and walked down to the sidings. I watched him stop, pick up a medium-sized plank of wood, and place it on his head. He then proceeded to walk forward, balancing the plank on his dome, hands out at his side. After the fourth step, he suddenly pivoted through ninety degrees, so that the plank lay across his head. Another four steps, and another ninety degree pivot, so he was facing whence he came and the plank was in line again. Twice more he did this until he ended up exactly where he had started, each time spinning under the plank, keeping it in the same plane. Then he carefully removed the plank, placed it exactly where he had found it, and walked out of the railway yard, leaving me standing in the shadows, mouth agape. As he passed me, he seemed to see me, and stopped.

'Forget it, lad,' he said, 'no one will ever believe you.' I don't know to this day if he'd set me up! And he was right, you know, they didn't!

Some of the more onerous duties a young probationer is subjected to in his early days relate to the mind-bogglingly boring hours spent 'in the office'. Usually it meant that when the cadet was off, you had to do the front office or the switchboard. I loathed that bloody switchboard. A grey and entirely bewildering instrument which comprises of one outside line and a bank of white 'flick' switches to a multitude of extensions. I couldn't ever get the hang of the thing.

Early morning on the switchboard was the very worst duty you could have to perform, because it invariably fell at a time when you needed to be out getting offences. An assessment was carried out every three months, and the workbook was checked to see if you were putting in the bread and butter jobs as well as the not so obvious offences.

One morning, at four-thirty, I know it was that time because I was just about to put the kettle on for the early turn cuppa, the light flashed on urgently in the console. Sighing deeply, I put the kettle down and flicked the switch to the answer mode. A very fruity voice came on, and introduced itself as the Chief Superintendent. Never having actually met the man, I had only had dealings with him in the past by putting him through on the phone to the boss's office. The conversation went something like this.

'County Police Office, Constable Woodhead speaking. Can I help you?'

'Morning! Well done, lad, like the way you did that. Very professional. Now then, Chief Inspector in?' Half-past-four in the morning? The boss in? Who is this looney?

'Er, no sir, I'm afraid he isn't. Er, who's speaking please?'

'What? Oh, Chief Superintendent here. You say he's not in? Why not?'

'Er, well, it is half-past-four in the morning sir, he doesn't usually start until about eight-thirty.'

'Damn! I told him to be there when I rang. He's supposed to call me later today and I need the information now. Urgent, you understand. Told him over dinner to be in early and ready to act. Now look, phone him up at home, will you? He'll probably be getting dressed to come down to the station. Catch him with his trousers down, so to speak, eh? Good man. Tell him to phone me at my home, he's got the number. But I must have the info before five o'clock. Right? Leave it with you then.' The line went dead with a click.

I stared at the switchboard. Well, here goes. I rang the boss's home number and waited. And waited. And waited. Probably having a shave, I consoled myself.

Finally the phone was lifted, and a very tired voice said, 'Chief Inspector K – What is it?'

'Oh, morning sir, PC Woodhead here. Just had a call from the Chief Super. He wants you to phone him before five o'clock. Says it's very important, and you know what it's about. Says you are to phone him at home. Said you know his home number. Is that alright, sir?'

'What? Oh yes. Didn't say what it was about, did he?'

'Er, no sir. Not to me. Just said he had to have the info before five.'

'Yes, right-oh. I think I know what it's about. I'll get right on to it.' The boss sounded quite excited, must be something big. I put the line down. No sooner had the light gone out, when it came on again.

'County Police Office. PC Woodhead. Can I help you?'

'Ah, well done, Chip,' intoned the same fruity voice of the Chief Super. And he's calling me Chip. *Must* have made a good impression on him!

'Quite had you fooled, didn't I?' The voice had changed to that of a colleague posted at an outlying satellite station.

'WHAT?' Panic now sets in!

'Hahahaha,' the voice chortles down the phone. 'Just been practising my impression of old – ' he gave the nickname of the boss in chief. It was rude and referred to a part of his anatomy. 'Anyway, took you in, didn't it?'

The cold hand clutches at my guts, and twists. Oh God, what have I done? The voice was going on.

'Yes, very pleased with that. Thought I'd phone you back to put your mind at rest. Bound to make you flap.'

'Well yes, Ken, it did that all right. Now would you like to phone the Chief Inspector and tell him?' A long pause from the other end.

'Er, you didn't . . .,' the voice trails off.

30

'I did,' a slightly sadistic note creeps into my voice.

'Oh shit!'

'I think that sums it up quite well, Ken. Yes, quite apt and to the point.'

'Oh shit!' The line goes dead, and I sit with face in hands as the light comes flashing furiously on in the console.

There are those who do not seem to have any inhibitions in their approach to either the telephone or public speaking. Their confidence oozes from them like hair oil. One of the senior bobbies was like that at another of my stations. Again I was on switchboard, a little more wise this time. However, I remember an incident which still makes me laugh when I think of it.

In comes me laddo, straight to the switchboard, and picking up the handset, casually asks, 'Er, what's the Chief Constable's number, Chip?' I'm not that daft!

'It's in the book, Len. Under the headquarters extensions. What do you want him for?'

The answer is a wink, a tap on the side of the nose with his finger, and a grin. I get out of my chair and hand the entire responsibility over to him!

Phone tucked under chin, he expertly flips through the internal directory, and then to my amazement and, I must admit, gleeful anticipation, dials a series of numbers. The phone buzzes, and I hear the voice of the Chief Constable's secretary faintly on the line. There next followed a conversation of such brilliant complexity and daring that I virtually committed it to memory as it happened.

Colleague, speaking in rough northern working-class voice: 'Ello. Is that the Chief Constable?'

The female voice squeaks something at the other end.

'Oh oh. I see. Well then, can I speak to him then? It's the GPO telephone engineer here. We've been doing some work on the extension to the Chief Constable's

31

office, it's been very crackly of late, or hadn't you noticed?'

The secretary squeaked something, probably in the affirmative.

'Aye, aye, that's right. Well it was in the dottling contact on the extension through relay. Anyway, it's fixed now, and we've checked out the line by way of test meters and standing currents, so that's alright. Now we have to do the phonetics testing, and that can only be done by him on his own extension. Well, that's not strictly true, the phonetics can be checked by yourself if you'd like to just pop in and pick his phone up. Won't take a minute, it's just a small sentence which contains all the phonetics in the alphabet which we check for clarity. Must get it right for the Chief Constable, mustn't we.' He's grinning into the phone, actually living the part.

'You can? Oh that's great, pet. Sorry to disturb him and all that. You're putting me through now? Lovely.' He looks across at me with seraphic face.

I mouth at him, 'You're a f . . . ing looney!' He grins, then is back on the phone again as the voice states in masculine tones that it is Himself.

'Ah, good morning Chief Constable. It's the GPO telephone engineer here. I've explained to your secretary what has been happening. You've been on leave, I believe? Yes, that's right. Pleasant time, I hope?' The man's a real pro – I can't help but admire his gall. I would have fallen apart by now, but he goes on.

'It's this phonetic test, you see, sir. Has to be done, according to Home Office regulations, due to the importance of your extension and nature of your position. You obviously understand.' The man's a miracle, not a falter.

The Chief's voice is now quite chatty, and he asks what he can do to help.

'Oh, it's quite simple, sir. I will give you a sentence

to repeat over the phone which contains all the phonetics we require to check the line out. Will you slowly and carefully repeat this sentence after me, emphasizing all the leading letters? It's "I CANNOT EAT MY CURRANT BUN". That's it sir, just that. All the C's and T's, you see? Ready when you are.'

Faintly I hear the immortal words spoken slowly and concisely over the phone. As they finish, a slight pause, and then, 'Again sir, if you wouldn't mind. Reading seems to be alright, but volume is a bit off. A little louder, perhaps?'

This is too much! The voice states the words again, louder and with greater clarity. He finishes.

'That's lovely, sir. Now, just once more at that. Thank you.'

Through the receiver I can hear, 'I cannot eat my currant bun.'

'THEN STICK IT UP YOUR ARSE!' The phone goes down with a triumphant thump!

I explode, and have to leave the room before I wet my pants.

3

Watch the Birdie

When you deal with sudden or unexpected death as often as a police officer does, it begins to become indexed in your mind under categories of nasty, unpleasant, tragic or unfortunate. There is never an element of cynicism or lack of feeling towards either the victims or the bereaved. It is a part of the job in which a young policeman learns about Life with a capital L. How strange, you may think, that death teaches about life. Not so, for you find yourself looking at life with a clearer outlook. In dealing with death, the humour must come through if it's there in any way. This does not make the death any less dignified, but usually refers to the events which follow death and the way in which the police officer concerned deals with them.

So it was that on one warm and sunny morning, Constable Dawkins was walking his beat in a provincial seaside resort, casually shaking hands with doorknobs and thinking of his wife in bed, breakfast, and his wife in bed! An early turn shift, starting at six in the morning, tends to make you think like that. He became aware of an elderly woman running towards him, waving her hand in an agitated fashion, and noted that she was in slippers, night attire, and curlers.

'Can I help you, madam?' he enquired.

'Oh dear, oh dear,' she sobbed into a rapidly disintegrating tissue, 'it's old Mr Starling. I can't wake him. I've called and called through his door, but he doesn't answer. He's *always* awake at six sharp, when I take him his early cup of tea. Up at six-fifteen and exercises his birds, then breakfast at six-thirty. Not a word this morning. Oh dear, oh dear, I'm sure he's dead.'

'Bugger,' Dawkins thought the word with venom, but kept a straight and concerned face.

'Alright, my dear,' he put a comforting arm around the lady's shoulder. 'Let's go and take a look, shall we?'

As they walked, the lady told Dawkins that her lodger, Mr Starling, had been with her for twenty-five years. 'Just a lodger, mind. Nothing more than that,' her eyes had glared defiantly at him and he held up an assuring hand and shook his head in disbelief at any other thought which may have sullied his mind.

They reached the front of the house, a well-kept and stately looking Georgian building that was snugly placed between the Midland Bank and the Rock Emporium, its noble façade facing directly on to the harbour. Granite steps, five in all, led from the pavement and up between two large stone portals which, in turn, set off the solid oaken door at the entrance. Bay windows dominated the front at all levels, of which Dawkins could see there were six. A tall, narrow building, but one which retained the opulent glories of its former sea captain owner.

They entered the large hall, carpeted in a floral Axminster, covered in thick, clear plastic sheeting. To stop little sand-covered feet ruining the pile, Constable Dawkins was told. The staircase was at the end of the hall, and led directly down on to it. The stairs were covered in the same clear plastic. They began to climb upwards, negotiating the octagonal landing of the spiralling staircase. After four floors, puffing slightly, Dawkins noted that the Axminster had changed to a fading Wilton without the benefits of clear plastic. Still good quality, he was told again, and nodded breathlessly.

The fifth octagonal landing saw the end of even the Wilton and became wooden boards. Polished every day,

35

said the voice of the owner of the varicose-veined legs he was following. Dawkins couldn't even nod.

'Bloody hell,' he thought, 'if the poor old bugger hasn't died in bed, it's a wonder, after all these sodding stairs.' His guide was still nattering on about Mr Starling and his birds. 'Probably pigeons,' Dawkins mused as a red mist seemed to float in front of his eyes, due mainly to lack of oxygen.

They arrived at a large door on a small landing, and his guide stood back. She stooped and picked up a floral cup and saucer placed by the door, and on standing, tapped on the door in timorous fashion.

'Ooohooh! Mr Starling? It's me, dear. Mrs Grimethorpe. Are you up, dear?'

No answer.

Dawkins rapped on the door with a little more force, born out of a kind of desperate and wishful thinking. 'Mr Starling? Are you alright? It's the police. Open up please.'

The silence was ominous.

'Got a key, Mrs Grimethorpe?'

'Oh dear, oh dear. I was afraid of this,' the tissue finally disintegrated into shreds as she blew into it, wiped her eyes, and attempted to tuck the residue up into her sleeve. Groping deep down into the folds of her dressing gown, she came out with a bunch of keys that would have done justice to a medieval jailer. Selecting one off the bunch, she handed it to Dawkins, and fled downstairs saying, 'I can't watch, I can't watch.'

Dawkins sighed inwardly. Unlocking the door, he pushed it open, and entered the room.

'BLOODY HELL,' he jumped back as, in a flurry of whirring wings, a multitude of colour, a cacophony of noise and a haze of seed husks about three hundred budgies lifted in unison and flew around the room!

His back to the door, Dawkins stared in disbelief as the multitude swooped and dived in bowel-evacuating panic around the walls and ceiling, to finally settle on to their various perches on the backs of chairs, sofa and, Dawkins noted with dismay, down the half-dressed outline of a man lying on the bed. A very fat man, judging by the way the little birds undulated in feathered outline down his body. Dawkins took his helmet off, and scratched his head. The rim of his helmet became the perch of two budgies as he did so, and as he moved forward to the body in the bed, his shoulders supported three more.

Dead. No doubt about it. Dead as the proverbial doornail. Heart too, judging by the colour. He checked the pulse. Nothing. Upper body cold, back slightly warm. He looked round the room and saw that the front bay window was outlined by a wire mesh and frame, into which was set a wooden frame door. The door was open.

It was obvious the old lad kept his budgies in the bay window aviary, and let them out for a fly around morning and evening. He'd come in last night, opened the door to the cage, gone to get undressed ready for bed, and collapsed. Good, no complications. Dawkins moved three budgies off the deceased's bulbous nose, received two sharp pecks for his trouble, and sucking his finger, covered the florid face with the sheet. The three displaced birds resumed their perch on top of the tent now made by sheet and proboscis. He turned and made for the door of the flat, flicking budgies off his helmet and uniform. His movement caused the whole flock to again lift in unison, sending a cloud of feathers and dust soaring up through the sunlight streaming in the window. Dawkins shut the door behind him, and with eyes closed, leaned back against the frame.

Mrs Grimethorpe had a little weep when she heard, but set about putting the kettle on in determined fashion once she had disposed of another tissue. Dawkins went out into the hall and called the station, requesting they contact him by phone. The phone in the hall 'tinged', and on answering it, Dawkins heard the strained voice of Allan Sommerford, his shift sergeant. Allan was suffering from his kidney stones again. They gave him gyp.

Dawkins outlined the death, emphasizing that there were no suspicious circumstances, and requested the coroner be informed, the shell coffin be brought round to the address and that a doctor attend to certify 'life extinct'. Allan Sommerford made careful note of request and time on the log, then told Dawkins to stay where he was.

Sitting in the large, comfortable kitchen, Dawkins made up his pocket book. He was now acting on behalf of the coroner, so a report was going to have to be submitted. His radio squeaked.

'Yeah, go ahead,' he sipped his tea.

'Kit? Allan here. Right then, the story so far. The shell is at Div. Headquarters, the doc can't make it till sometime after nine-thirty, the GP man has just gone sick, and I can't raise the coroner at his home number, so I'll have to wait until nine. I can't book a post-mortem until he requests it, so everything is in limbo until after nine o'clock. What time's your meal?'

'Er, nine o'clock?' Dawkins slid a piece of hot toast into his mouth, and sipped on his tea again to wash it down before he had to speak again.

'Ten four. Take your meal, and I'll do what I can in the meantime. Out.'

At home, Dawkins was halfway through his bacon and eggs, when the radio bleated again. 'Kit? Allan. The shell will be at the nick by ten. The doctor is on his way down and requests you join him there at the house. The coroner wants a post-mortem unless the doc can sign it off, and I'll see you at the house about ten o'clock. It's just you and me, though, with Frank going off. Can you get going?'

Dawkins gulped his tea down before answering.

'Yeah. Ten four.' He kissed his wife on the cheek, and warned her he might be late home. She shrugged her shoulders and turned back to the sink. After all, they were only taking the kids to the beach for a picnic.

Arriving at the house, Dawkins began to climb the spiral staircase, joining the doctor on the fourth landing. The doctor was leaning on the bannister, puffing and looking as though he needed his own services.

'How many bloody flights are there, Kit?' he eyed the disappearing stairway upwards with something like fear in his face.

'About two more, Doc. What's the matter? Forgot your crampons and oxygen bottles, then?' Dawkins grinned into the scowling face.

Pulling himself laboriously upwards by means of the bannister, the medical man climbed the last two flights, to stop, chest heaving, at the door to the flat. 'This it, then?' he wheezed.

Dawkins opened the door, and the doctor walked in as Dawkins closed the door quickly behind them, gleefully watching the doctor's face.

'What the F . . . !' The non-medical term was accompanied by frantic arm waving and head bobbing as the multitude lifted in fright at their sudden appearance. Dawkins grinned evilly.

'You SOD!' The doctor glared at him. 'You might have told us!' He waved away an errant feather that slid slowly down his nose.

Still grinning, Dawkins showed him the body, and sweeping irate budgies off their perches on the deceased, helped make a perfunctory search of the body for signs of injury.

'Dead,' the doctor stated finally, 'probably heart. No history, other than 'flu five years ago. Mind, if he had to climb all those bloody stairs every day, I'm surprised he lasted this long!'

'Can't write it off, then?' Dawkins was ever hopeful.

'Afraid not, Kit. Not even my patient. Sorry.' The doctor grinned back at him.

'Shit!' Dawkins stated.

'Quite!' the doctor answered, and in a cloud of husks and feathers, they left the room.

Allan Sommerford arrived just as the doctor was leaving.

'Morning, Doc,' Allan nodded in greeting.

'Morning, Al. How's the kidneys?' Allan was one of his patients.

'Giving me hell. Can't wait to go in and get these stones removed.'

'Won't be long. In the meantime, no lifting heavy objects,' the doc waved a warning bunch of car keys in the sergeant's face.

The sergeant and the PC manhandled the shell coffin up the winding stairway, being particularly careful not to touch the new wallpaper as Mrs Grimethorpe directed from the hall. At the top, the sergeant stopped and leaned exhaustedly on the bannister.

'Oh bloody hell, Kit! I'm shagged.' His grey colour confirmed this fact. Dawkins didn't have the heart to play the same trick on his sergeant as he had on the doctor.

'Er, the room's full of budgies, Sarge.'

'Full of what?' His colleague stared at him.

'Budgies.'

'Oh well, it makes life interesting, I suppose. Best keep my hat on,' and with a dejected slump of the shoulders, he stood aside as Dawkins opened the door, and wrestled the coffin through into the room. The small birds again lifted off, and the two officers made their way through the haze of feathers and seed husks to the bed.

Mr Starling was a big man – very big. Most of it beer gut, such that he was almost as tall lying down as he was standing. With the utmost difficulty, his body was slid into the coffin, which was of a fibre glass construction, light and flexible. It had to be, because his gut stood proud of the rim. Sitting on the lid, the two officers managed, accompanied by posthumous farts from the interior, to close it sufficiently for the front clips to be secured on their wobbly fittings. The rear clips were missing, and Bunjee cord stood in as the substitute.

They slid the coffin across the floor, Dawkins pulling and the sergeant pushing, both going slightly bug-eyed at the effort. Reaching the landing, Dawkins pulled the end of the coffin over the lip of the stairs, and with feet splayed into the stairwell corners on either side, took the strain. The deceased weighed in at about sixteen stone, and this weight was delicately tipped down the stairs until he lay at an acute angle downwards.

Slowly the two officers began to negotiate the steep stairway, one step at a time. Suddenly Allan Sommerford groaned, and letting go of his end, straightened up with a look of complete agony on his face as his hands groped and pressed in the region of his kidneys.

Dawkins, his eyes bulging like a boxer dog's balls, strained forwards and up as the full weight was taken on his one hand, the other grasping the bannister with white knuckles. The handle gave a dry 'crack', and to his horror, he watched the coffin comply with the laws of gravity. He groped feebly as it passed through his straddled legs, but merely slowed its descent a fraction as he pulled the Bunjee cord off with a loud twang. Staring in disbelief between his now empty thighs, Dawkins watched as the shell bounced and clattered its way around the first landing, with a dry ricochet on each wall, and disappeared with deceptive slowness over the lip of the next flight. Dawkins set off in pursuit.

The next floor, being carpeted, merely served to accelerate the downward plunge of Mr Starling's last journey, and Dawkins was fast losing ground. He was still dashing wildly down Wilton, when the shell hit plastic-coated Axminster, and the cause was lost.

Wild-eyed and in a state of exhausted shock, Dawkins managed to keep the elusive rear end of the coffin in sight, as it whistled with silent speed across the hall and towards the open front door. The doorsill presented only sufficient drag to shake the straining lid clips free of their pressure, and the lid flipped off as the shell sped on its way down the granite steps and across the pavement, to come to a halt smack up against the side of the transit van parked outside. On its course, it had cut a swathe through the holiday makers wending their happy way to the beach past the front door.

The coffin stopped, but not so Mr Starling. His momentum was such that, there being nowhere else to go, he was thrown forwards and upwards. A loud belching groan emitted from his body, and with arms akimbo and flailing, the corpse sat up! Draped over the lip of the shell, the florid and wide-eyed body groaned out its trapped gases.

Dawkins was in time to see this final flourish, and noted also, as if in a daze, that two women slipped quietly down to the footpath in dead faints, and one man held his hand over his mouth as he turned away. Picking up the lid which was lying by the door, Dawkins dived down to street level, and slammed the top on, spinning the round body into a prone position as he did so, and then with what he hoped was an air of nonchalance, sat with crossed knees on the lid. The pandemonium raged, as Allan, the colour of the Georgian stone portals, came staggering to the front door. Dawkins suddenly had an awful thought.

'Allan,' he shouted in panic, 'did you close the flat door?'

A child, wide eyed at the sudden appearance of body and policeman, suddenly looked up, his beaming face radiant. 'Look Mummy, look,' he shook his comatose mother on the pavement, pointing with podgy finger. 'Look Mummy, look. Pretty birds, Mummy, pretty birds!'

Over Allan's head, three hundred multicoloured budgies flew to freedom over the harbour!

4

Ashes to Ashes

Can you imagine two sets of policemen from different forces on opposite sides of a surging river watching the swirling antics of a dead body trapped in the ebb tide? It did happen, on numerous occasions, when we had more city and borough forces. A dead body becomes the responsibility of the force and coroner in whose area it finally rests. With it comes the messy business of recovering said deceased in whatever stage of decomposition, and taking it for a post mortem which, in the old days, was always attended by the coroner's officer.

Should the ebb tide push the body towards the city banks, the borough policemen would be patting themselves heartily on the backs. However, it was not unusual for the city bobbies to get a long pole or piece of wood, and shove the luckless corpse back out into mid stream again, to the accompanying shouts of 'cheating sods' from the opposite bank. They in turn would then scavenge for a similar prodder, and walk with the tide ready to shove it off again. And so it went on!

On one occasion, I witnessed a colleague who had the misfortune to be on the beat when a body was brought in by local fishermen, trapped in their net. It had become ensnared some two miles out to sea, but they brought it close into shore, and asked a holiday maker on the beach to call the police, mentioning the body. Word went round the beach like wildfire, and so it was a luckless officer who arrived at the scene to find the whole area packed with sightseers! What was worse, the fishermen were some twenty yards out. Al waded out in his uniform, trying to appear nonchalant. He had asked for assistance, and as I was on the adjoining beat, and hugging myself in glee at his hapless task as it came over the radio, I was ordered to attend and help!

Arriving at the beach, I ordered the crowds back, and called to Al to see if he wanted any help. 'Get out here Chip. The body's caught in the net. It's been in the water for some time. Have you got a big bag or something?' Damned silly question, I thought, slipping my boots off and rolling my trousers up.

I waded out to Al, who was wrestling with a mass of ropes and net holding a well-decomposed corpse together. Giving an annoyed wrench, Al pulled at a loose bit, then watched in dismay as the head fell off and disappeared down to the bottom of the sea!

'Oh f . . . g hell, Chip. Look what's happened.' Al was groping around on the sandy bottom in panic. The vision of him trying to explain the missing head to the coroner, plus the circumstances in which we now both found ourselves in front of about 2,000 people, gave me a fit of the giggles.

'Don't stand there f . . . g laughing!' Al was thrashing about in earnest by now, 'Do something.'

'I'm not diving under the water to look for a bloody head. It's bad enough me having to stand with my balls freezing in water, without doing your job for you.' I was adamant, not to say exceedingly cheesed off.

Al suddenly disappeared under the foaming brine, and emerged gasping and blowing like a whale, holding the errant head above his own as he emerged like a prehistoric sea monster. It grinned with lopsided and toothless mouth at the fishermen, who vomited violently over the side of their boat.

'Hold it, Chip.'

'You must be joking, chief,' I shuddered.

45

Elated that he had found the elusive head, Al tucked it under his arm for safe-keeping, as he tried to find a suitable hole in the net in which to put the head and keep the body intact. The old song, *With Her Head Tucked Underneath Her Arm* flashed into my mind, but it did not seem an appropriate time to whistle it. Finally getting the net free from the boat, we towed the grisly load behind us towards the beach. The crowd fell back in horror.

The carrier van, a large transit with blue light flashing, came down on to the beach, and swung round with panache through the crowd. The shell was floated out to us, and pushed under the body. We lifted it out of the water and placed it into the transit, slamming the doors to hide the nasty sight. The crowd applauded as we dived into the front. With a blip of the throttle, we drove away to the sound of their applause ringing in our ears.

The luckless individual who had fallen in the sea, apparently from a passing Panamanian tramp steamer, could have had no idea of the problems he was going to cause after his demise. But who else in whatever job, would have to suffer the indignities we suffered that day, and yet find some humour in it? Callous? Not really, but any humour in a situation like that shines through like a rainbow after a storm.

Funny things happen on night shifts. During the day-light hours, there are usually more people about at any one time than can be imagined, and yet, more happens in a shift between the hours of ten p.m. and six a.m. with fewer people. An eight-hour day shift can be very boring, and yet, at the start of a ten to six shift, you *know* something will happen before the end. It doesn't matter what night of the week it is, something is bound to happen.

Domestics, for instance. That is the title given to any

incident which involves people in their own home or street. Neighbours fighting. Husbands beating wives and, don't laugh, wives beating husbands. All manner of feudal disputes.

When you receive a complaint from a wife about her husband, then you know that whatever happens, you are going to lose! There are no rights or wrongs in the issue. You, the bobby, are going to come off worst.

You attend the house, the wife is in tears, the husband sullen and probably most unwilling to even let you in. What can you do? Enter the house to prevent an arrestable offence? Prevent a breach of the peace? Don't make me laugh! You go in, they both start off at each other, he becomes threatening, you step in, and *she* tells you to piss off and keep out of their family argument! It's true! If you do lock the old man up for whatever reason, she is back next day asking to withdraw her complaint.

Some officers have their own way of dealing with domestic situations, usually in a manner which would have their bosses sitting with their hands in their hair pulling large tufts out with accompanying hysterical giggling.

I once heard of a bobby who had a large beat in a detached, rural area. He was the scourge of the area, a man who dispensed justice at the ends of his fists. He is long retired, but having had the pleasure of working with him for a short period prior to leaving the force, I have no reason to dispute the tale.

He attended the scene of a 'domestic', a small country cottage where a young labourer and his wife lived. They were in one of a pair of cottages, the other was occupied by the man's in-laws. First sign of trouble, and round to Mum went the girl. Now, Constable E knew that the lad was a bad lot when he was in drink, and so was expecting the worst when he went round to answer a complaint from the mother-in-law one Thursday evening. (Thursday was Market Day for the livestoc market and pubs had been open all day from ten o'clock.

Walking into the mother-in-law's cottage, he sees th young lad slumped in a chair facing the fire, and his wife weeping in the opposite chair. One look at the girl's face showed that she had been clouted in no uncertain fashion. There was a bruise on her face the size of lemon. She was, at that time, also heavily pregnant Constable E looked at the girl and said, 'Did he do this to you?' A tearstreaked face nodded feebly.

'Why did you do this to this little girl?' he asked the sullen youth.

'Because when I came home from the market, she' not got my dinner ready. So I belted her.'

'You belted her? Just like that?'

'Yes, just like that,' the face and attitude was defiant.

'Well now, just come out into the hall a minute wil you. I want a quiet word and I don't want to involve your wife or mother-in-law.'

He walks into the hall and round towards the kitchen, just out of sight of the weeping girl and her distraught mother. The youth follows. There is a sharp 'thud', and a slim body slides along the hall lino until just the feet are showing at the other side of the door. Constable E looks round the door. 'G'night, Mrs G., g'night, Mrs L. See you next Thursday?'

'Yes, thank you, Mr E. Same time next week.'

It's so ridiculous it *has* to be true. However, back to night shift.

One night, I'm on patrol, pounding my lonely vigil. The narrow streets are shrouded in fog which is getting thicker and making the street lamps cast a ghostly green light about the cobbles and old shops. It is in the old part of town, which has retained its nineteenth-century character. The cobbles are glistening and the damp cold is seeping through my mackintosh. Now, I am one of those who firmly believes in wearing what is issued at

48

the correct time, and our force still has capes. Well, us older ones have still retained them since issue. Now the old cape is very useful. You can put your hands in your pockets under it and no one can see. You can secrete a lighted pipe under it and no one can detect a wisp of smoke, and they are very, very warm. So, I put on my cape. High collar keeping the draught out, tucked well into beard, and helmet well down over eyes. Now find an empty doorway. Lovely, just the job. Only half an hour to meal break.

A drunk weaves his way down the street, a mumbled song breaking from his lips as he staggers and ricochets from lamp post to wall to doorway to lamp post. Head down, he peers closely at his watch, and has three attempts to focus before lighting, or attempting to light a fag. I love watching drunks. They really are lovely and all follow a pattern of striking a match, searching for their fags with the wrong hand in the other pocket as the match slowly burns down, opening their cigarettes by shaking the packet until one comes proud, burning their finger on the match, pocketing their fags to light another match, and so on. And all the time humming and singing whatever song it is that's in their mind at the time. They talk to themselves as well, explaining to their brains what their bodies are currently doing, then they break back into the song again, not loudly, just at that level where they and I can hear it. Smashing. This one is doing all of that, and from the vantage point of my doorway, a deeply recessed opening into a craft shop frontage, complete with bottle-bottom glass in the windows, I watch with interest as he weaves three steps forward and two back towards me.

I step out and say, 'good evening.' A pleasant and, you would have thought, fairly innocuous thing to say. Not so. He looks up and sees me. He stops and a look of sheer horror comes over his face. He takes a step back, and clutches at his throat as his newly lit fag drops from apparently nerveless fingers. A gurgled, strangled cry leaves his lips as he staggers backwards away from me, colliding with some force against a lamp post.

'Oh f . . . g hell! No! NO!! Keep away from me. Aaaaagh!' He turns to try and run, but his feet overtake each other and he falls over.

'Hey! Come on now, old son. What's the matter with you? Had a few too many. I'm not going to lock you up.' I try to placate him as he pushes his hands at me in an effort to keep me at bay. He stops when he hears my voice.

'Bloody 'ell. You're real,' he pokes me with a wobbling finger to confirm his discovery.

'Yes. What did you think I was.'

'Wha' did I think? WHA' DID I THINK? I thought I'd walked back through a bloody time warp, tha's wha' I thought. You come out of that old curios, curiosy curisotigy shob looking like a copper from the turn of the centururury, old high collar, cobbles wet, writhing fog, beard . . .' he gropes for his handkerchief and laughs nervously.

'Thought I was a ghost, did you?' I laugh.

'I bloody did!' he's belligerently emphatic about that point! I laugh quietly, and as he turns away to look for his fags again under the light, I step quietly back into a dark alley, and walk on childish tiptoe away from him! Drunks? I love 'em.

A friend of mine in the Liverpool force told me of a funny happening on night duty which apparently involved one of his mates, so take this one for what you will, but it goes like this . . .

The copper's walking his beat, checking the fronts of lock-up property in a shopping precinct, when he hears a noise from round the back. He walks quietly round to the rear of the premises, when he sees two men acting in a most friendly manner towards each other. He turns his torch on them, and says,

'Right! just what do you think you're bloody well doing?'

As it's obvious what they're up to, they break apart from their clinch, and one of them turns and runs off down the alley in a clatter of dustbins. Grabbing the remaining one, the copper starts to walk down the alley after the second, but it's obvious he's flown.

'Right,' says the copper to the tremble lipped youth, 'I've got you. Two consenting adults over the age of twenty-one in private. That is not what I saw, was it?' He glares at the youth who is on the point of fainting away.

'No,' he squeaks.

'So you're for it, my lad. And if I could get my hands on that lad who's just scarpered, by God, I'd lock him up too. But first I'd ram my peg right up his arse till his nose bled.'

A small and effeminate voice comes from the darkness, 'I'm in the bin.'

Made me laugh, too.

Night shift is a killer, there's no getting away from that. It's debilitating, it plays havoc with the digestion, ruins the constitution, not to mention one's sex and social life, and buggers up the metabolism completely. Ask any night shift worker. The only thing in its favour is that you can take your time in walking around and the meal breaks tend to be more chatty as you try to stay awake.

One night I was in the office, and on shift with a very senior bobby who was a legend in my force. He's long retired, but it was my privilege and, indeed, my honour to have worked and served with this man. Honest as the day is long, integrity which glowed, but with a streak of impish humour in him that gladdened the heart of any bobby who listened to him recall a tale from thirty or more years ago.

We were sitting in the front office, having our meal-break about half past two in the morning. Danny, looking at me from over his wire-framed specs, poured out two mugs of tea the colour and consistency of black treacle, and said, 'You're very much like me in my younger days, Chip.'

'Thank you, Dan. I take that as a compliment.'

He sipped pensively from his hot mug, and said, 'Have you ever hated anyone so much you wanted to get rid of them?'

'What? You mean do them in?'

'No, just get them out of your life. Away from you completely.'

'Well, there's one person I could think of, but it's only wishful thinking.' I made a joke of it.

Danny leaned back in his chair, and looked at a spot on the ceiling with a faraway mist over his eyes.

'I had a sergeant once,' he began, sipping his tea pensively, 'who I hated so much I wanted to kill him. That bastard rode my back for two years, all the time. I was single then, and the sergeant concerned is long dead and gone, so I don't hurt anyone with this tale. He really was the Devil incarnate. I could never do anything right, I was always on the mat for some minor disciplinary offence. He belittled me in front of the public. He was an absolute sod!' Danny looked fiercely over his specs at me, 'A SOD!'

'You didn't like him then?'

'That, my young friend, is an understatement. I loathed him. So much so, I decided to get him out of my life. I contrived to injure him in such a way that it couldn't be traced to me, and whilst he was off sick, I would put in for a posting. So I devised a plan,' he crunched quietly on a biscuit for a while.

'This sergeant used to ride a bike. Especially on

nights. He would ride it very quietly, and swish up behind you and demand your pocket book for inspection. He'd ride it quietly up to your point and try and catch you out. He'd ride it down alleyways to try and catch you talking to a colleague on another beat. He whizzed here, there and everywhere on that bloody bike. Always to try and catch you doing something you shouldn't. He did this to me for two years on top of everything else. So, I contrived a plan. I watched him during night shifts and he seemed to follow a set route. I was at S – (he named the place, and I know it well, having served there two years myself) and as you know there is a point at the top of the hill where, on a bike, with a good shove off, you can ride all the way to the old police station without ever touching the pedals once. Nearly three miles. There's just that one sharp corner to slow you down, just before you cross the canal bridge.

'I watched and waited, from one point in an alleyway just off the towpath. I could see his front light as he started his downward trip, heard his tyres as he whizzed round the sharp corner and watched him zoom over the canal bridge at a tremendous rate. He always went up to the top of the hill to check on the bobby on that beat and catch him walking halfway up the hill with two minutes to get to his point. Always the three o'clock point in the morning. Then, after waiting for the point time to come round, he would ride back down to the poor struggling bobby, and walk back with him to the point, rollicking him all the way, and until five minutes past that point time. Then, with a monumental shove and two hard pushes on the pedals, down he would come to make the station for quarter to four and his early cup of tea before the lads came in. No integrity, that man. Anyway, I'm wandering off the story. I'd got a long length of tarred rope, there was always some on or near the towpath, and decided to stretch it across the road at wheel height between the first stanchions of the bridge. I'd lie it on the road when he went up the hill, and when he came down again I'd lie in wait in the alley, with my end looped round the upright on my side and fastened tightly on the far side. Then, from the darkness, I would wait until I heard his tyres swish round the corner, pull it taut, wait for the crash, and then dash to the scene. In the confusion of the crash, I'd cut the rope free, and throw it over into the canal, where it would sink from view. Then I'd summon an ambulance and be the hero of the hour.' Danny sat back and put his feet up.

'But Danny, you might have killed him. How would you have lived with that on your conscience?' I was beginning to get worried, it sounded like a confession of murder to me.

'Well, that did cross my mind, but I was obsessed. I'd had enough! So I waited for my chance. The next night shift, we used to work a week at a time then, I found my length of tarred rope, and hid it in the alley. I checked my lock-up property, made my points, and saw him ride over the bridge up towards the hill. Then I nipped over to the bridge and secured the end of the rope, draping it across the road and looping it once around the other upright. Then, giggling in a maniacal fashion, I ran into my hole. I saw the light come flying down the hill, and disappear away behind the warehouses out of view. I listened hard, and heard the tyres swish at the corner. I leaned back on the rope, pulling it taut,' he leaned forward and lifted his cup to his mouth, swallowing deeply and with relish.

'Don't just bloody sit there, Danny. What happened?'

'The rope was taut as a bowstring, and I kept the pressure on. Then there was a horrendous crash, the sound of breaking glass, and silence. But I was still leaning back on the rope with nothing happening. No tugging, no pulling, nothing. I tell you now, Chip, the silence was eerie. I waited a few minutes, then walked nervously up to the bridge. There was my rope, still there, but no sergeant, no bike, nothing on the other side. I was flummoxed! I undid the rope and chucked it over the bridge into the canal, then started to look for what had made the noise I'd heard. I found it, right on the corner. There was the sergeant's bike, on its side, all mangled up with the back wheel still revolving slowly, tick, tick, tick. I heard a groan, and right on the other side of the road I saw the sergeant, lying in a huddled heap, his helmet all flattened where he'd hit the wall at amazing velocity. His arm was broken too, so I called the station from the callbox on the corner and asked for the inspector and an ambulance. Then I went back to the sergeant. He was just conscious.

'What happened Sarge?' I asked him.

'F . . . g tyre burst on me, right on the corner,' he groaned.

I covered him up with my cape, and went across to look at his bike. Sure enough, the tyre was flat at the front wheel. But it wasn't punctured, though. No sign of a tear or rent or nail. 'But,' here Danny finished his tea with a swig of triumph, 'the bloody valve was loose!' He looked at me with that impish grin of his, eyes twinkling behind his spectacles.

'Someone had had the same idea as me, but they were far, far more subtle.'

5

There's Many a Slip

It was a freezing cold night as I stood at the dimly-lit telephone box which represented my point at the far end of my beat. Set up on a hill, it commanded a superb view of the town and harbour far below me. However, the wind driving in off the North Sea made the eyes water so much as to obscure the view, and come to that, any forward vision after about two seconds' exposure.

I wrapped my greatcoat tighter around my throat, sharply aware that the temperature was falling very quickly. It had been below freezing most of the day, and when I had come on shift at ten p.m. the news had forecast it even colder by midnight. I shivered, and was grateful to see the supervision Escort turn into the road in which I stood, and pull up alongside me.

The inspector, a large gruff man, begrudgingly opened his window about half an inch, and asked for my pocket book for inspection, which I duly posted through the tiny gap. Blowing on my hands through my woollen gloves, I watched as he scrutinized my work and signed it with a flourish. The book then re-appeared through the slit in the window, and the inspector's voice came booming through after it.

'Shocking night, Woodhead,' he stated obviously. 'More bad weather to come.' This statement was borne out as a flurry of rain and sleet swept across the harbour below and rattled with venom off the car roof and my helmet.

'Bloody hell,' the inspector glared venomously at the windscreen, 'bloody awful! I wouldn't send a dog out in this!'

'No sir,' I said dejectedly, blinking at the fury of the squall.

'Well, must be off,' the window clicked back with emphatic finality and, with a casual wave, he disappeared through the enclosing downpour.

I began my patrol through the housing estate, towards the main road. I felt, rather than saw, the road surface turning distinctly icy, and immediately regretted wearing my ex-Forces ammo boots. Warm and waterproof, well bulled and with steel heel and toe segments, they were all leather. Ideal for appearances, but not a little useless in icy conditions.

By the time I reached the main road, the road and footpath surfaces were covered in a sparkling, shining coating of sheer ice. Grasping the stone wall which followed the hill down into the town, I realized that I was in trouble when my feet led my body by three paces with me leaning back in desperation to maintain equilibrium. It was no good. I either stayed there, or devised an alternative method of getting down.

The hill on which I perched dropped sharply away from me, crossing the tributary which ran into the main tidal river by means of a bridge which was built such that it was part of the hill. Across from the bridge stood the local night club, which was lit warmly and invitingly. I reckoned that if I could make the bridge, then I could negotiate the little footpath which led to it along the high river bank, and once there, gain access and a bit of sanctuary, in the warm foyer of the club. With this goal in mind, I began to control a sliding descent downwards by gripping on to the wall. I was doing nicely, when my radio called my number. The inspector wanted a road report. I stopped, and with one hand selected the transmitter from my greatcoat pocket. I answered his enquiry with my boots slowly sliding down the footpath, and finished my report somewhat more abruptly than was considered proper. My boots suddenly went, and so did I, sending the radio soaring up into the air as I thudded down on to the flagged pavement. My helmet, that most useless piece of police equipment, came off and gyrated in delicate circles down the hill towards the bottom. I gripped my fingers into a minute crack in the wall and prayed. This was ridiculous! I groped my way up the wall until I was in a crouched position, but decided that I couldn't stay hanging on the wall. So I let myself go, maintaining my crouched 'little man' position, and dug my gloved fingers into the unyielding concrete slabs. My speed appeared to be fairly well regulated as I trundled down the slippery slope, and all was well until I saw the drunk reeling his way out of the club and wending his way across the footpath to the main road. His inability to walk steadily appeared to counteract the instability of the icy conditions, and he made very good progress until he got to the ice-covered pavement. He slid slowly down the hill a short distance, leaning at an angle until he reached the bridge parapet. He stopped, and stood in stark magnificence facing the river, his knees braced against the parapet wall. He then proceeded to pee over the bridge wall.

Despite my predicament, I was incensed at his antisocial behaviour, and shouted at him as I continued to travel downwards. He turned his head, in an owl-like fashion, and watched as I approached him in my crouched walk. However, I hadn't reckoned on the build-up effect of ice on my gloves and boots, and being intent on the drunk's actions was unaware that my speed was increasing. I approached the drunk, travelling quite fast, and dug my fingers in hard to enable me to stop. Nothing happened. Well, that's not strictly true, one hand dug in harder than the other, and I began to slowly turn round. The drunk also followed my progress as he reached the limits of his neck turning, and his shoulders began to follow suit. I clattered past him, by now facing him in my 'little man' squat, but still intent on telling him off. We were facing each other as I passed him, and he was already twisted from the waist up watching me in owlish bewilderment.

'You are reported for urinating in a public place,' I stated with as much dignity as I could muster, as I shuttled past and continued with increasing speed down the bank. By now I was travelling backwards, so we were still locked eye to eye. His body must have been under tremendous stress as he tried to follow my progress with the continual twisting of his body. It didn't occur to him to unwind and watch my progress from the other direction, he just continued turning. Finally, the torque loading on his knees was too much, and in horror I watched as his knees and feet suddenly pivoted in the direction of his body, and he disappeared backwards over the parapet of the bridge! One minute he was there, the next, gone!

Frantically I tried to scrabble forward on hands and feet back up the hill, as I continued to plummet downwards. The whole effect must have appeared hysterical to any casual watcher. In fact, it was.

The stupidity of one's act is directly proportional to the number of people who witness it, and I must have appeared monumentally stupid! The pub at the bottom of the hill was just turning out, and the regulars were astounded to see a member of the local constabulary approaching them backwards at quite a speed as he attempted to scrabble forwards.

I came up against the wall of the Electricity Board generating station with a thud, and the locals slid and slithered themselves across the road to my aid. I explained to their concerned faces that I was not mad, and that a man had fallen over the bridge. Together, we all struggled back up to the bridge and peered cautiously over the parapet. Nothing!! Not a bloody sign! They all looked at me pityingly, and then laughing hugely, all slid with childish abandon down the hill and home, leaving me staring goggle-eyed in disbelief over the parapet.

I tried to explain to them as they clattered away, I *did* see someone go over the edge, but got the distinct impression that they thought the only person over the edge was me!

Their hilarity faded into obscurity as they all drifted away, and it was then, faintly, I heard a 'lah lah'ing and drunken humming coming from under the bowels of the bridge. My drunk staggered, muttering, across the frost-hardened mud of the small river and on to the frozen river bank of the main river and out of sight round the corner.

But how?!

I looked down in disbelief. There, below me, was a large boat. In the state of being repaired. Covering its deck was a huge tarpaulin, suspended such that the owner could work under it and be free from the elements. My drunk had landed right in the middle of this tarpaulin. I looked wildly around for a witness, anyone! But they had all gone. No one to see that I wasn't a looney. Even the drunk had gone. I clung miserably to the parapet, feeling a sob of self-pity welling up in my throat.

Inclement weather conditions play a great part in a policeman's life, to the point of governing his workload and course of action over a complete shift. Constable M was being governed thus, one Christmas Night.

The weather had been cold, and he started his evening shift at his detached beat office by phoning in for any orders which may have been issued during the festive day. No news is good news, and he was told to stay at home and enjoy the rest of Christmas Day unless required. He did just that! Uniform jacket off, and slippers on, he resumed his chair in the lounge. His wife poured him a large whisky, and curling his fingers round the crystal tumbler, he laughed at the antics of Morecambe and Wise on the television.

Suddenly, the phone rang. It was the Control Room notifying him that a colleague was in trouble at a disco some distance away, and required help. Swallowing the whisky in one fiery gulp, he leaped from his chair, donned boots and jacket, and raced out to his minivan. Despite the cold, the engine fired immediately, and he reversed off the drive and out on to the main road. Concern for his friend prompted him to put his foot down, and approaching the small market town en route to the trouble spot, which was in a barn some four miles on the other side, he selected the blue light.

Entering the town, he saw the road surface was streaked with lines from the traffic that had gone before him, noting with horror that these lines crisscrossed all over the road surface in what appeared to be uncontrolled skid marks. This was borne out a few seconds later when he saw three cars in static collision. He also noted, with rising panic, that his speed was over sixty m.p.h. and there was no way he could stop! He took his feet off all the pedals, and as he whizzed past the startled members of the public, he prayed that nothing would come out of any of the side entrances on to the main road. He was still doing fifty m.p.h. as he left the town centre, blue light still flashing, and horribly aware by the way the van was skittering that the road was a sheet of black ice.

Ahead of him, he saw the slow-moving rear lights of a Morris Marina, and a quick glance at his speedometer showed that he was still doing forty m.p.h. Pulling out very cautiously some two hundred yards before reaching the Marina, he managed to get past without mishap. He was still going at thirty. He was past the Marina, but on the wrong side of the road, when he saw the right hander approaching him. Still doing twenty-five, he entered the bend, managing to wrestle the van around by the seat of his pants. At twenty he saw the left hander, but also felt the rear end of the van begin to overtake him. In a flurry of grass and mud which seemed to obliterate the windscreen in a tumult of noise that seemed to him to last ten minutes, the van and its luckless occupant leaped and bounded across the frozen verge, to come to a halt in an equally loud silence, tipped at an angle in a ditch and parallel to a hedge.

He sat there, shaking.

His first reaction was to get out before the van caught fire, and he tugged in desperation at the passenger door. It was jammed! He would be burned alive! Oh God! Then he realized that the door was merely locked, and the van was in no danger of either exploding or catching fire. He reached for the radio handset, and in a shaky voice notified the Control Room that he had been involved in a County Vehicle accident. Assuring the operator that he was uninjured, Constable M gave his location and asked for some assistance. Putting the handset back, he then realized that in the quiet sanctity of the cab, there was a distinct, and strong, smell of whisky! Oh God! That last drink! He felt the cold stab of fear clutch at his gut, and groped in his pocket for a cigarette. To his delight, he found a packet of Extra Strong Mints! Oh, happy day! He popped three in his mouth and chewed frantically.

He then became aware of the lights of a car approaching, and round the corner came the Marina. It slithered to a stop opposite him, and the driver got out. There was a swishing 'thud' noise, and Constable M watched the driver execute a supreme somersault and crash to the road. He got out, and walked to the edge of the verge, still chewing furiously on his sweets. The other driver groaned, and then propelled himself across the road, seated. Once upright, and obviously unhurt, he asked Constable M if he was alright. Assuring him that he was, Constable M detected a distinct smell of peppermint on the man's breath!

Returning to his own van, the constable called the control to inform them that the road was covered in black ice, and extreme caution was to be shown by anyone attending. Receiving their affirmative, he was then aware that a blue light was flashing urgently on the road approaching them.

The sergeant's car came towards them, and Constable M waved it down in an effort to slow its approach. Undeterred, the Escort came to the scene, braked, and with hissing tyres and illuminated brake lights, disappeared from view round the corner and out of sight! There was a slight 'crunch' noise from behind the hedge, and the sergeant's car came creeping sheepishly out backwards to pull up on the grass verge. The sergeant got out, and with the same sickening thud previously heard from the Marina driver, executed a very similar somersault and landed on his back.

'SHIT!!' It seemed to sum up the situation quite well.

The sergeant regained the verge, and steadily walked his way over to Constable M with deliberate tread.

'Bloody awful,' he stated in a voice which trembled, and with breath which also reeked with the strong smell of peppermint!

His car had sustained minor damage to the front offside wing, and as he and the constable and the Marina driver exchanged extra strong mints, they saw the lights of a Road Traffic car coming at speed towards them. Blue lights aflash and two tones blaring, it zoomed up to the scene. And went past! And continued out of sight and hearing! There was a faint and muted 'thud', then complete silence.

The one-eyed traffic car returned, a little slower this time, and stopped at the scene. By now, Constable M was beginning to feel distinctly better about the situation! The doors opened, and with almost unparalleled delight, the two officers and their civilian cohort watched as two white caps flew upwards, and the wearers descended.

'F . . K!!'

'SHIT!!'

Both expletives were simultaneous!

The two traffic crew members slithered their way to the safety of the grass verge, and continued to swear in peppermint-flavoured language for a few minutes. Seeing the sergeant, they seemed to stop drawing attention to their words and breath, talking in subdued tones with heads facing the other way.

Constable M was by now positively ecstatic!

They moved the van out of the ditch, apparently unharmed by its jaunt, and with a casual wave of his hand, the civilian skated across to his car. 'Merry Christmas,' he called as he slowly drove off.

The three officers each selected their respective packets of extra strong mints and offered them in turn to Constable M. Then in convoy, they made their way back to the station to make out reports. Pulling into the yard, they saw the original cause of the emergency call getting out of his van, and talking earnestly to the Chief Inspector.

'Oh no!!' Four mental voices spoke as one. The Chief Inspector was a Methodist by repute.

They all nodded to him, and he silently acknowledged their presence as they walked in a dejected line to the office.

'Evening sir,' the sergeant spoke to a picture on the wall in the opposite direction to the chief, and coughed into his hand such that a peppermint was popped surreptitiously into his mouth. Constable M nodded glumly at his colleague.

'Everything alright, Wilf. Not hurt, are you?' He

belched and winced as the whisky fumes seemed to reek over the whole office.

'No, I'm OK. It was nowt nor nothing,' the strong peppermint-coated voice came back to him. He blinked!

The Chief Inspector was talking to the traffic crew and the sergeant, with hands over his face, as if in silent prayer. Then he looked up.

'Gentlemen,' he stated sadly. They all looked round at him. 'Gentlemen, as you know, I do not drink. In fact,' they could all feel the tension mounting, 'in fact, I never touch the stuff. But, tonight I was at a dinner party. I am ashamed to admit that I did have three large helpings of a very strong sherry trifle. It did seem to be only a slight deviation from my beliefs. But, I am aware that this could be construed as drinking. Now, all I can smell or taste is sherry! I feel awful about it, but what is worse, I have an interview with the Chief Superintendent in half an hour. What do I do?'

Five packets of extra strong mints were held out to him in sympathy.

6

Wet Noses

The policeman's job is one which involves up-dating and re-training from time to time. The law, or even basic knowledge of the job, is now becoming so very complex that courses of various types are running most of the time in various forces.

Every police officer is qualified in First Aid, requiring these 'on the spot' skills for a variety of reasons. Usually on the occasion of either a road traffic accident or acting on a report of someone collapsing in the street or home. So, in order to maintain this high degree of efficiency for helping the injured, courses are held every so often to keep the officer's training up to date.

Whilst this next anecdote is not strictly to do with police work, it does concern my experience on a police course, and has caused me to suffer from the ribald remarks of colleagues at the drop of a hat since.

I was down for a First Aid training programme, which was to take place at the Headquarters and last two days. I was going down with a cold, and knew it. Dry, tacky throat, sneezing, running nose and watering eyes. I was sure that my temperature was running at 109°, but also knew that if I didn't attend, I would have to go at a later date which, knowing my luck, would coincide with something far more important.

On the morning of the first day, I groped my way in watery-eyed misery around the bedroom, eventually finding the handkerchief pile on the ottoman. I miserably grabbed at two off the pile, and placed them, one in each pocket. The weather outside was awful. Howling sub-zero winds and freezing cold. I didn't feel any better when I was collected by my colleague in the car for transporting to Headquarters. The heater was full on, which was a comfort, and seemed to dry my cold out for the duration of the drive.

Arriving at the Headquarters car park, we drove around for a while looking for a parking space. As with all centres of bureaucracy, every space seemed to be held in reserve for someone of obscure position but higher rank than PC. Finally, if you think of the Chief Constable space as A.1, we found a minute gap in Z8002! In fact, it would have been quicker to park the car at our home station and walk.

I got out of the car, and the freezing wind hit my wheezing and cough-racked frame like a mallet. Eyes spouted like twin fountains, and my nose ran in torrents. Great explosive sneezes thundered from me with leg-staggering force, and I had used up my left-hand pocket handkerchief before I had even made it to the trades-men's entrance. Snuffling pitifully, I groped my way through the corridors of power to the gymnasium, where the lectures were to be held. The warmth of the gym, coupled with the fumes from the indoor swimming pool next to it, gave me a few minutes of unmitigated hell. I ignored the faint voices breaking through my tortured brain, and sniffing violently, tried to stem the constant flow of liquid from my eyes and nose. I didn't want to use my stand-by hankie until absolutely necessary!

We were called to the centre of the gym, into a cosy and intimate circle of police persons, and our tutors introduced themselves. I was sandwiched between two very attractive policewomen, who were most concerned about my health. I sensed, rather than felt, the explosion of a 'sneeze-and-a-half' begin to mount in intensity, and groped for my right-hand pocket. There was no other way out, the 'stand-by' would have to be used!

'Aaaaaaaachooooooooooo!!' the effort knocked me sideways, almost doubled over, but I had managed to trap the bulk of the explosion under the cover of my handkerchief.

Groaning feebly, I held the handkerchief to my nose, and, amidst the hysterical shrieks of laughter from my fellow students, except the young girl on my right, into whom I had cannoned, focused my eyes on the instructors. It was only when I saw their faces, and heard the ribald comments about 'not being able to leave it alone' and 'whatever turns you on, Chip', or 'wouldn't think someone his age would be so kinky', that I saw with horror that I had, clutched firmly to my nose, lacey, delicate and sexy, a pair of my wife's white knickers!

Word must have travelled quickly, because on returning to my section after the course, I found a box placed on my locker with a large red cross on it. Opening it, I found to my horror a pair of skimpy black lace knickers, an old bra and a delicate slip inside, together with a note that stated – 'Just in case you get the flu!' Thanks lads!

Some courses have an educational flavour to them, especially if they are by way of attachment to other sections. This usually occurs early in the police career, and gives some guidance to what specialist work can be undertaken by the fledgling PC when he has finished his probation.

Such a course was the attachment to the Dog Section. A week is spent in this idyllic situation, away from the fuss and bother of normal police work.

I arrived at the Dog Section for my attachment, and was immediately accepted with warmth and good humour. The dogs were due a training session, and the day began with mass grooming. I watched as the handlers went to a shed, and came out with a bucket, comb and stiff brush and made their way down to the large kennels block. Brush and comb were held in one hand, and bucket in another, as each of the handlers walked towards their respective kennel to see to their respective dogs. Shouting and whistling, they let their dogs know they were coming, and it was a heart-warming sight to see the dogs lolloping round the pens, tongues lolling and eyes bright and laughing with greeting. Some time was then spent in patting, wrestling, and generally playing with the dogs.

After the greeting, the bucket was placed, upside down, on the kennel floor, and each dog would gambol up eagerly and place its front paws on the upturned bucket bottom. Then would follow a friendly, settling-down period of grooming and brushing, together with genial chat from master to dog, with the occasional choc drop to aid the *esprit de corps*. Great fun for all concerned. Except for one handler.

He had collected his bucket, comb and brush, but everything went into the bucket. In his other hand, and held out of sight up his back, was a great length of two by two wood, like a club.

Morosely he made his way to his dog's kennel, whistling in half-hearted fashion to an enormous Alsatian. This dog leaped and gambolled round his pen, eyes rolling in ecstasy and great tail thumping and thudding the floor and walls in happy greeting. The handler opened the door, and braced himself to accept the onslaught of canine pleasure.

It was obvious that he had a good dog, and that he also felt some great affinity with the beast, but his attitude was difficult to work out. I mentioned this fact to the Dog Section sergeant.

'Right!' he said with a grin, 'watch on, and see why.'

Down went the bucket, bottom uppermost. Down went the brush and comb, all done one-handed. Up went the dog's front paws on to the upturned bucket. Up came the brush in the right hand.

'Woof!!' went the dog, and secured its great fangs with some force and, indeed, great accuracy into the handler's right wrist, which, I noted, had been fitted with a leather wrist guard.

'You bastard,' roared the handler, and the piece of two by two descended with force on to the dog from behind the handler's back!

Effing and blinding the dog, the handler slashed and swished the great cudgel in huge sweeps, driving the dog back into a corner. It cowered, and once it did, the handler patted it, slipped it a coughdrop, and the grooming continued without any further disruption!

The sergeant grinned.

'Best duo in the force, take all the prizes for tracking, crime work, searching buildings, you name it, they can do it. More arrests than any other team in the area. But every day it's the same. He comes in, the dog bites him, he belts the dog, the dog submits, and then they're off. But every day, he gets bitten. The tragedy of the thing is he's got that dog every day for the next eight years!'

I was touched by the way I had been accepted into the fold at the Dog Section and, over a cup of tea, was musing at what a jolly good set of chaps they seemed to be. My reverie was broken by the sergeant who informed me that the training session was about to start in earnest, and that everyone was so pleased I was there, as it meant that they wouldn't have to be the target criminal!

I was then taken into a huge field, where the full complement was set out in a long line of handlers and dogs, the latter sitting with tails swishing and mouths 'smiling'. At me!

I was dressed in a padded pair of kapok-filled trousers and long leather boots. Over my shirt was placed a very thick pullover, a felt pad, some half inch thick, which I noted with panic rising, came down the length of my right arm and right down my back to the base of my spine. Next came a leather chest, shoulder and arm guard, studded and hinged, which was strapped round me and fastened. And finally there was an ego-boostingly large leather pouch which I strapped over the marriage equipment and round the waist. Didn't do my ego a lot of good, though. I would have needed balls like a stallion to do the space justice! On top of the whole ensemble went an old police uniform jacket.

I was pointed out towards the centre of the field, and with lumbering gait, told to walk across the field diagonally. With heart thumping, I did as I was told.

'Stand still,' came a command. 'Stand still or I shall release the dog.'

I did *exactly* as I was told.

'NOT YOU, YOU F . . . G TWIT,' another voice roared, which I recall as being that of the rather charming sergeant. 'THAT ORDER IS TO GET THE DOG ALERTED TO THE SITUATION.'

Judging from the baying and slavering set up by the hounds, I didn't think they needed too much alerting! I continued walking.

'YOU! STAND STILL OR I'LL RELEASE THE DOG!' I fought down the rising urge to fall over and lie dead.

'Right, go get 'im.' I saw the leash on 'hound one' slipped, and the great slavering beast was after me, the rest of the pack barking and snapping encouragement.

'F . . . G RUN, YOU PRAT! GIVE HIM SOME-THING TO CHASE AFTER!!' I needed no second bidding, as with lurching steps I attempted to reach the sanctuary of the fence which bordered the field. No chance!

About eighty pounds of diehard Alsatian hit me on the run. It was like being hit by a runaway railway engine in the back. Fangs a foot long locked into my arm, and I was bowled over. The arm was then apparently to be torn off and returned to the handler in one piece, because that's what the dog was intent on! Writhing on the ground, I was twisted this way, then that, until the breathless handler caught up with us. The dog was called off, and circled me, barking. I sat up, winded and shaken, holding my head in my hands.

'Well done, lad,' the sergeant was beaming. I felt immediately better, as he went on, 'Bloody good job. Well done. Best one we've seen.' I looked out at the world in gratitude through splayed fingers. The sergeant was patting the bloody dog and congratulating it at the same time! Me, I had just been cannon fodder! I did that bloody run five more times that morning, each occasion being about the same in result and intensity of pain! I did have a gun to fire on the last time, but that only aggravated the hound into biting the balls cover off whilst I was on the ground!

At the end of the day, I mused that it was no wonder that you hear of policemen being bitten by police dogs at demonstrations. After all, they're trained to bite at the arm of an old police uniform!! Next time you see a demonstration on television where the dogs are involved or let off the leash, you just watch. When the dog is slipped, the only person running is the real thief or demonstrator. Every policeman will be frozen into immobility!

7

Wide Load

Sid Chaplan walked into the police office, and nodded a greeting to the sergeant at the desk. A nice little nine to five day to round off his week, then three days off. Just the job!

He picked the keys up off the board and signed out the area car in readiness for the shift, then made his way to the muster room for briefing. He read the logs and signed them, then picked up the flimsies which informed of what, if anything, was to take place during some or all of his shift. He was scanning them with interest when the sergeant walked in.

'Morning Sid.'

'Morning Sarge,' Sid sat back and raised an eyebrow. 'Not exactly overrun with manpower, are we?' he nodded round the empty room.

'Ah! Bit of a problem there, Sid old son. Two gone sick, one on post mortem. Result? You, me and the cadet!' The sergeant raised his eyebrows to the ceiling.

Sid grunted.

'Have you read the flimsies, Sid?'

The constable nodded and waved them aloft in reply.

'Right then, you will have seen that there is a wide load coming through the town at ten-thirty. Seventy-five tons and eighty feet long. Going through the centre, across the bridge and out on the coast road to some-where up north. I think it's Teesside. Anyway, it's got to come through here due to road works on the A1, and a series of low bridges en route. We've just got to see it clear through the town, and get it parked up on the layby on the north side for Humberside to take it over for escort. Our Traffic are dealing with that, so you just go ahead and clear the junctions, and generally keep the traffic to one side. OK?'

Sid nodded.

The sergeant continued. 'At eleven o'clock, there is a civic reception in the town, when the Mayor is to open the new toilets. Apparently it is something of a "do", as the bogs have been awarded some diploma with regard to their architectural design. So, the boss is going with his missus, and the Lord Lieutenant as well. Shouldn't present any problems,' he crossed his fingers and rolled his eyes. 'I've got Reg to come in at eleven instead of two, to try and help cover. Till then, you're on your own. You can take the cadet with you as observer, get the lad out of the office.'

Sid nodded glumly. He grabbed his board, and made his way into the yard to do his inspection of the Cortina. Just as he was completing it, the cadet dashed up, red faced and eyes bright.

'Morning, Brian.'

'Morning, Sid. I'm with you this morning.'

Sid winced at his puppy-like excitement, but closed the bonnet and refrained from comment. He drove the Cortina out of the yard, and down into the town, noting that even at this early hour, the town was filling up fast with both traffic and pedestrians. Most of the carparks were already full. He checked his watch. Nine-thirty. An hour to kill. He turned the car into the long drive which led to the sea front, and checked out the sands and the tide times. Parked up on the front, he made his book up for the previous day, then checked the flimsies again. Wide load time of arrival was ten-thirty. Three miles an hour. One mile through the town, twenty minutes. Good! Bit of leeway. He relaxed.

Ten-fifteen saw Sid and the cadet parked up at the 'one mile roundabout' at the edge of town.

'Used the radio before, Brian?' he turned to the cadet, who was desperately trying to look like a policeman, glaring at the traffic under his peaked hat.

'Er, yes. Once or twice,' the lad nodded.

At ten-thirty-two, there was no sign of the wide load nor its escort, so he called the Control Room. He was informed that the load was half a mile out, and as they spoke, Sid saw the blue lights of the approaching escort. The Granada sped down to their location, and the driver pulled alongside.

'Morning Sid. It's all yours,' he shouted through the open window. 'There's been an accident on the A1 and we're the only mobile on.' His observer grinned across at Sid.

'There's about three miles of traffic behind this.' He gestured backwards with his thumb, 'all blowing their horns and trying to overtake. You're welcome to it.'

Sid shrugged and slipped the car into gear. Headlights on and blue light flashing, he waved as they shot off, and drew out smoothly into the carriageway in front of the load.

The drive down into the town was relatively uneventful as, with arms waving, they cleared the oncoming traffic. The trouble started when they entered the one-way system into the town centre. The road narrowed considerably, with high buildings converging on either side. Sid judged the load would just about scrape through. They had just entered the narrowest bit, when Sid checked in his mirror at the following load. To his horror he saw a large coach pull out to overtake it, followed by a stream of cars all bearing roof racks and drawing caravans on the back. The load ground inexorably on, and the coach was halfway past when the driver realized his mistake. The result was inevitable. Suddenly there was no room. Coach and load were side by side, hemmed in by buildings.

'Oh bloody hell!' Sid stopped and got out. 'Why does this always happen to me?' He kicked at a tin in the gutter.

The cadet walked alongside him, face worried.

'Er, it's a bit tight, Sid. The time, I mean.'

The lorry driver and his mate were in verbal battle with the coach driver, and they had just got to the point where the lorry driver was rolling up his sleeves over very brawny arms as Sid approached.

'Did you see this dozy sod?' A defiant chin was thrust out of the window at Sid.

'Quite so, quite so.' Sid was beginning to get agitated too. 'Just reverse up a bit, driver, will you?' This to the coach driver, who selected reverse and slowly started to go back a bit. His movement was stopped by the violent and almost hysterical blowing of a horn from the car and caravan behind him. Sid went to the car driver.

'Can you reverse up a bit, please?'

This elicited the same hysterical horn-blowing from the chap behind the caravan. It also started a clarion call of horn-blowing all the way back. Sid sighed.

The load inched its way into the narrow bit of the one-way system, until it was tight up against the stationary police car. It stopped. The road behind was still blocked, locked solid, but shuffling the traffic an inch at a time had made the minutest gap.

Sid walked back to the police car, then stopped and stared in disbelief! A gold-coloured Vauxhall Viva was parked directly in front of his car! Facing the wrong way, locked and apparently abandoned! Sid clutched his hand to his head.

Now *he* couldn't move! A traffic warden approached, and began to write down the details of the Viva in his book.

'Where's the bloody driver, Mac?' Sid asked.

'Dunno Sid, I've just come across it,' the traffic warden stuck a ticket on the windscreen and walked off.

'Oh Christ,' Sid looked wildly around him.

He espied the cadet.

'Brian, get on the radio. Tell them we're trapped in this bloody jam, we can't move and we want some assistance. Can you do that?'

'Righto Sid,' the cadet leaped into the car and grabbed the handset.

Sid looked up the road, and felt his heart sink as he saw a Rolls Royce, a large black Daimler and the Chief's Volvo far in the distance, trapped in the traffic.

'Well, he's going to be too late to open the mayoral bogs!' and for some reason Sid found the situation really quite funny!

He returned to the car in time to hear the cadet say on the radio, 'Assistance required please. We are trapped in this pile up of traffic.'

Technically it was right, but to the operator, it sounded as though the car was trapped in a pile-up. Sid groaned and, glaring at the cadet, grabbed the handset off him.

'Belay that last message. We are trapped in traffic with a wide load. Can you get us some assistance?' Nothing! He tried again. Again, nothing. Only the operator requesting all traffic mobiles in the town area and surrounding area to attend their location as they had a report of a pile-up involving a police vehicle, the occupants of which were trapped. Fire and ambulance had been notified and were attending.

Sid looked disbelievingly at the cadet, who had found something very interesting in his nails. Sid tried again, but still no luck. Above the din behind him, he could faintly hear the 'deedahs' as the fire brigade and ambulances turned out to the scene. He grinned wryly and shook his head.

A shadow appeared at the window, and out of the corner of his eye, Sid saw the cadet slide down under the dashboard with his hands over his head! He looked up, and saw the boss. Red of face, and chins wobbling in anger, he was tapping his gloves on his leg. Sid grinned up at him. There was little else he could do.

'It's not bloody funny!' The old man was very cross.

'No sir.' Sid couldn't help himself. The radio was going mad, and fresh deedahs could be heard coming from other routes into town.

The Chief's face was darkening to a purplish shade.

'The High Lord Lieutenant and his lady are stuck in the traffic, as is the Mayor. They'll never get to the toilets in time.'

This last statement, made admittedly under stress, was the last straw! Sid laughed.

'Bursting are they, boss?' He shook at his own joke, feeling the tears spurt as he tried to suppress his laughter by biting his lip and freezing his cheek muscles. The Chief was still going on.

'Everything's stuck,' he stated, but the statement only made Sid think in terms of matters lavatorial, and he snorted through his nose.

At this point, the Mayor and his lady, both resplendent in full regalia of chains and plumes, walked past on the footpath. The sight was so out of place, and looked so ridiculous, Sid exploded. He just couldn't suppress it as he watched all the dignitaries wending their way towards the mayoral bogs.

'Stop laughing!' The boss's moustache was a-quiver, and his chins shuddered. Sid thumped the steering wheel in his efforts to get his face straight. The deedahs were closer now, and Sid looked up at the boss's face. It was no good! He wound up the window, and pushed the button down. The boss's face was puce! His mouth was opening and closing, wattles leaping, the radio was screaming about pile-ups, the deedahs were coming from all around, the cadet was crying, and round the corner came a fireman with a hosepipe! Sid slid hopelessly down the seat and under the wheel, all semblance of self control gone!

The events that followed caused Sid to continue his paroxysm of uncontrolled shrieks of laughter. The sight of the Lord Lieutenant's anxious face peering in the window, with his tricornered hat almost gave him a hernia! The lorry driver finally bopped the coach driver as he attempted to complain to the Chief. Officers appeared from all angles. Sid shrieked at them all!

He tried to explain to the Chief Superintendent later that morning, but when he'd asked Sid what had happened, Sid started again! Three attempts Sid made, and when he finally finished and was wiping his eyes with the back of his hand, the old man said, 'Grounded; three weeks. Posted in four. 'Oppit!'

'Yessir. Where to?'

'Traffic!'

Sid was helped from the office.

8

The Old 'Uns
are the Best 'Uns

In this job, a lot of time is spent in dealing with the problems of the young or the elderly. With the former, it usually concerns matters relating to crime or damage to property, with the latter it is spent in generally keeping an eye on them and giving them advice when something is troubling them. Sometimes, sad though it is in a society which prides itself on its caring attitude, a policeman is the only person some of the elderly see from one day to the next. He passes their window 'on the beat', and after a while they look out for him just to wave or receive a smile. You become 'their policeman', and a good beat bobby knows there is always a cuppa on the go if he needs one. That, and a chat. They see everything, those house-bound pensioners. The old ladies can cook like a dream, and most of the old men have gardened all their lives. In my garden, even as I write, there is a display of the most beautiful dahlias given to me some time ago by an old lad, which were surplus to his 'show growing' requirements. They stand now, deep red and yellow, smiling at the sun from against my fence. My old friend is dead now, but they are a constant reminder to me of his cheerful outlook, his knowing wink when I was invited into his potting shed, and his roguish chuckle when he thought he had a rival beaten hands down in a forthcoming show.

One dear old soul on my beat was Annie. She was about eighty-six, and lived all alone in her tidy little bungalow under the shadow of a ruined castle. We became great chums after she had telephoned the station to say she had received an indecent telephone call.

I went down, and told her to keep a referee's whistle by the phone which, if she blew hard into the mouthpiece, would have the caller on the other end reeling in circles with his eyes going like cherries in a fruit machine. She was delighted with this piece of sadism, and as the sports shop was on my beat, I got her a whistle during the day and popped it in to her.

The next day, I called in to see if her mysterious caller had phoned again as he had done the previous evening. She sat me down in the comfiest chair, and poured me out a cup of tea, smiling in a conspiratorial manner.

'Well, Mr Woodhead,' she confided, 'he did ring again. About seven-thirty. Do you know what he said? He said, "I know you. Oh yes, I know you. You are the lady who makes lovely gravy. Do you know what I would like to do to you? I would like to spread your lovely gravy all over your body. Then I would like to lick it all off."

'So I said to him, "You dirty little beast, take this," and I blew my whistle down the telephone as hard as I could, dirty little devil. He didn't know me, Mr Woodhead. I know that now!'

'How can you be so certain, Annie?'

'Oh that's easy, Mr Woodhead. He kept talking about my gravy. I have meals on wheels.'

Another old character was Arnie. He was about ninety, and as fit as a fiddle up to the day he died. He suffered from a cleft pallet which gave him a booming speech impediment, an affliction he maintained was received from one of the Kaiser's bullets when in the trenches. His claim to posterity in this book was the manner in which he got his beer allowance during the week. He

81

would sit in the bar from seven o'clock until closing, having ridden down to the town from his cottage on a rusty old boneshaker of a bike, circa 1927.

In the bar, he would look out for a newcomer, and, having seen one, would introduce himself to the delight of the locals and the embarrassment of the visitor. Arnie would then take out a matchbox from his battered jacket pocket; it was always the same type, those manufactured and advertised under the 'Pioneer' make. With the latest sucker concentrating in rapt attention so as not to actually see the local laughing, Arnie would draw four circles on the back of the box.

'How many pies are there drawn on this box?' he would boom. The luckless person would shake their head sheepishly and answer, 'Four.'

'How many?' Arnie would leer in conspiratorial manner around the bar. 'I bet you a pint there's more.'

His victim would agree to a pint, just to get rid of him.

'There's five!' Arnie would boom triumphantly. His victim would rise to the statement. 'Five?'

'Ar! One, two, three, four on the back,' he would spin the box in his gnarled old hand, 'and another pioneer!' Cackling, he would claim his pint to the merriment of all gathered.

We went through a ritual every Friday night, Arnie and I. He would wait until the last minute before leaving the pub, usually right up to the time I visited the premises on a duty call. He would be at the singing stage by this time, and with booming deference to me, 'Goo'night Cunsable', he would lurch out to his faithful old bike leaning against the wall. Then he would climb aboard, and with wobbly wheels and long, thin legs which were fitted into old army boots, push weakly down on squeaky pedals and ride off towards home.

Some time later, I would be patrolling in my minivan down the road he took, and would look hard at the hedge which bordered the sharp right-hand corner outside the village. Sure enough, there it was! Arnie's rear reflector twinkling out at me from the hedgebank. I would stop, ear cocked. Arnie's booming rendering of *Blue Spanish Eyes* would come floating over from where he had landed and I would pick him up, he protesting his innocence strongly, and place him in the front seat of the van. His battered old velocipede would be slung in the back, and I would deposit both him and his bike at his front door. Bike leaning on the wall, and Arnie sitting against the front door. Then I'd ring the bell, and run like hell! Arnie's wife, Elsie, was a tartar. At eighty-two she wielded a wooden spoon like a battle axe! I would be pulling away as she opened the door and began to berate her old man with the spoon. Marvellous couple.

Old Arnie was a bad 'un up to the day he died. When he went into hospital after a bad fall, I popped in to see him when I was on 'nights'. The nurses loved him, but as the sister said to me, 'For all his ninety years, Chip, he's a bugger with the nurses. Can't keep his hands to himself! You bend over him when he's asleep, and find he's been watching you since the start of rounds through half-closed eyes. You're no sooner bent over, then – *whoosh*! – he's up the back of your dress! Wicked old sod!'

He died suddenly, and it was only afterwards, when I went in to deal with an accident case, I heard of his end. He had been fading fast, struggling for breath and lapsing into long periods of unconsciousness. There was a little Chinese nurse on the ward, who had taken Arnie to her heart. Checking his pulse during the early hours, he was very close to death and she knew it; she leant over to him as he struggled to say something.

'What's the matter, Arnie love?' she bent over him, then shrieked! His hand had shot straight up her legs under her uniform and pinched her backside! A dry cackle, and he was gone! Good old Arnie, I miss him even now.

We often get calls from concerned neighbours about the elderly people living in their area. Usually it's because they haven't been seen for a few days, or the milk has been left outside, or the curtains aren't open. When we attend, we are left with no alternative in some cases but to break in. Often the cause is because the old person has fallen down and can't get up again, so we are able to help. Thanks to good neighbours.

On one occasion I was asked to attend an old lady's house. She hadn't been seen for two days, and neighbours were concerned. En route, I was picked up by the sergeant, a smashing young fella who is destined to be a darn good senior officer one day. We turned up at the house, a very nice bungalow in lovely condition with a beautiful garden. The bungalow itself was recently modernized, such that all the windows were double glazed with huge panes of plate glass. Every window.

We called through the letter box, and peered through the glass, but could see no sign of movement. The doors were locked from the inside, not a good sign, and none of the neighbours had a spare key. So, we would have to break in.

The only window which did not seem to measure more than six by six feet was that in the back door. Left with no alternative, I drew my staff and after many hard wallops, managed to break the glass with a horrendous crash. The key was in the back lock, and opening the door, we began a systematic search of the house.

Kitchen, clear. Hall, clear. Lounge, clear. Dining room, clear. Master bedroom, clear! Spare bedroom?? Clear!! Bathroom??? Oh God, clear!! Nothing.

As we stood in the shambles of the immaculate kitchen, the front door opened. In came our old lady, fit as a flea! We mumbled out our rather pathetic explanation, told her we would arrange for a glazier to attend, and covered with embarrassment, stumbled from the house. We were halfway up the footpath, when she called out to us. 'Young man! I don't want this fobbed off! None of this "We could smell gas" business, because I'm all electric!!!'

We had, of course, been given the wrong address. It was 32, not 23. We were forced to break entry there as well, but were in time to save the life of an old lady who was suffering from diabetes and had forgotten her insulin. So, all was well and we were covered, but I must admit to being very nervous about breaking into houses since then! I have spent ages just paring out putty from round a window frame so I can lift the glass out in one piece, carefully handing it to my colleague for safety, only to see it being leaned up against a wall out of the way and slide down with a crashing finality on to the footpath and split across the middle!

On another occasion, I was asked by a local doctor to break the door down to gain access to a flat in which an old gent had collapsed. Being a karate buff and practising ju-jitsu for twenty years, I was often called for such efforts of demolition! A loud yell, and a good forward kick had the desired results, and door, doorframe and half the flat wall plaster fell into the hall. The doctor dived in, and the old man was saved. But the damage was dreadful! I chased that doctor all over town for two days just to get him to sign an entry in my pocket book stating he had ordered me to do it in order to save life!

9

Strike it Rich

During my time in the force, I have been involved i
industrial disputes and public order incidents of gradu
ally worsening degree as the years passed. It is not fo
me to comment on types of police deployment, I hav
my own views on how matters were handled at the time
and admit that I saw only one side of the problem
Suffice it to say that the police role in any of these type
of deployment is to uphold the law of the country, a
defined and laid down by the duly elected Governmen
of the time. A bit bland? Possibly, but to deviate fron
this means that personal feelings encroach and cloud th
issue.

However, this type of policing, like it or like it not
needs a very specialized form of training. It only need
one bobby to take the law into his own hands and yo
have an 'incident'. So it is a training which involves
large degree of semi-military expertise, including horse
and dogs.

Now I don't particularly like horses. Oh, they're very
nice to look at, or pat, but they have the most anti-socia
habits! Especially when you are forced to stand behind
them! Someone said they were the most efficient form
of direct conversion of grass to manure, but omitted to
add that the conversion causes gaseous by-products
which are far more deadly at close quarters. They also
give me hayfever!

And so, the training day arrived when we were to

work with horses for the first time. Our general training had always been fairly well organized, with nicely appointed smoking breaks and cups of tea at suitable times; policemen get withdrawal symptoms if they are not fed tea at half hourly intervals – I remember seeing a colleague go into 'cold turkey' at an hour, too awful to describe.

The horses were brought on. Great lumbering brutes, they were. About sixteen hands high and all muscle. We all lined up, linked arms and awaited the orders to break ranks and let the horses through. On doing so, as they came through at the gallop, I found myself confronted by the wide expanse of the biggest equine arse I have ever had the misfortune to view from so close a distance. This backside was mine to follow for the duration of the exercise, and I glowered in its general direction through eyes which had begun to run from the minute it had come into close proximity! The tail I watched with baleful suspicion. Every twitch had me skittering backwards, to the annoyance of the men on either side of me! Suddenly, the damned animal lifted its tail just as we surged forward at the advance. I say 'we'; I, in fact, was being dragged by the sheer force of thirty men all linked arms in a forward direction. The horse moved slightly slower, and with the lift of the tail, it produced a fart of such incredible force and odour that a third of the line stumbled and fell back.

'Come on, lads – forward,' came the rallying cry of the boss, who was, I noted, well clear of anything nasty, and standing to the side. The keener element moved forward, pulling myself and ten other choking and gagging officers along with them! The fart had obviously been a musical overture for the second act, which at close proximity fell out in copious quantities, directly in our path.

There then followed a push and pull situation whereby

everyone was trying to get out of the way of the steaming heap, and by so doing, getting their neighbour into it.

This opening movement by the horse in front of me was the signal for the rest of his colleagues! Soon the ground in front of us was littered with piles of steaming dung, from which there was no escape. Especially for me. Streaming with hayfever, I was pulled, pushed and generally jostled into every pile of gunge in the area. That didn't stop the other lads from being subjected to the other obnoxious strainings emitted with ear-deafening noise, but at least that was the lesser of two evils.

By the end of the exercise, I was three inches taller than anyone else, and would, by merely walking over my garden in my boots, probably have the best roses in the county. The only consolation to my predicament was that the boss, laughing gleefully at my discomfort, patted the horse concerned and had his foot trod on by one huge steel-clad hoof!

With all the controversy about the use of police horses in the recent past, I can only say that there would have been worse complaints, although probably more effect, if they had sent the damn things into the fray backwards after a meal of wet grass!

Training is never like the 'real thing', and policemen acting out the part of picketers or rioters can be far more violent than the real thing. I'm afraid that many old scores were settled during those training periods, with senior officers running wild-eyed about the place as they saw the rioters over-running the 'line', or the 'line' beating hell out of the rioters/pickets! I well remember one occasion when we were undergoing shield training, and one of the 'opposition', dressed in denim overalls, dashed at the shield line and started beating the shields with a huge shovel. This was to increase the confidence of the men behind the shields as to the robust nature of the perspex. The senior officer informing us of this was not, I hasten to add, anywhere near the shield front line at the time! Anyway, in comes chummy, and there was a general muttering from the ranks as to what would happen to him, and the senior officer, if any of the shield holders were hurt, bruised, had watches broken or whatever!

The shields in the middle of the line were clashed and thumped with unlimited violence when suddenly, the ranks broke and the shovel and 'picket' were hauled into the mass of bobbies. There was a dull 'thud', and the shovel flew over the shields to land with a clatter on the ground in front! A defiant silence fell over the whole shebang, as the bosses stared at the shovel, the silent ranks and the fixed expressions of the shield parties. Baby blue eyes all turned up to the skies, and a tuneless whistling set off an air of complete innocence!

Summing up the situation in one glance, a sergeant in the middle of the ranks shouted, 'Tea break,' and as one, the whole lot broke off and went for a cuppa! Nasty incident averted! But the shovel was dispensed with in all future training. Mainly, I think, through lack of volunteers!!

For all the training we did, most of it was later superseded by the 'psychological' approach, especially in the 'real thing'. I don't think that anyone who has been involved in any of the public order situations in recent years, can look back in all honesty and say that there was one incident which really stood out.

My lasting memory of all during the miners' strike is of acute discomfort, long hours, boredom, sleepless days and nights, and probably the worst constipation I have ever had the misfortune to suffer!

However, as in all police work, the humour came shining through.

Like the time when a large contingent of men were deployed from all over the country, and after hours of discomfort riding in transits, trying to doze when there were twelve of them installed in a van which was designed to take ten average-sized men, not policeman size, seated on one inch of foam set on to slatted seats. Anyway, most dozed fitfully for the six-hour journey, and when they awakened at their destination would have been forgiven for thinking the driver had taken the wrong turning somewhere en route! The main notice board which announced their location was written in Russian! The poor men had not realized that they were actually being billeted in a Ukrainian Resettlement Centre! And after six hours in a transit van, bursting for a pee, who was there in their midst who knew the Russian for toilet?!

The next thing that met their eyes was a hall of minute dimensions which was laid out with four hundred camp beds, end to end across the width of the room!

Now, to be fair to the Ukrainians who had settled in the UK and set up the camp, it was devised as a youth training centre and had been taken over for the Police at short notice. Subsequently, the beds were those used by the Ukrainian youths at their camps, and as their average height was five foot six the beds were of according size. The average policeman is six feet tall, so it could be seen that there was going to be a good deal of overlap! Similarly, the spaces in between the beds was about eighteen inches. Officers also noted that there were five wash basins and four toilets, and it was April 1st!

The first night was something of an ordeal. The men were informed that they would be starting duty at 03.00 hrs the following morning, so it meant they would have to be up at 01.00 hrs. Some took to their beds early. Others decided on a few pints in the local pub. Others even more determined made their way to nightclubs in the local city.

Subsequently, as the first in bed were dozing nicely, the eleven o'clock drinkers were coming in. On went the lights, to sounds of cursing from the sleepers who had only just managed to drape their six foot plus lengths over their beds. A brief interlude of scrabbling as the lights were extinguished and men tried to undress in the dark in between the close-set beds, then another respite. At midnight and for periods afterwards, the lights came on and off as men returned from the clubs! Combine the whole ghastly business with the effects of several pints of beer followed by a pie and mushy peas supper and you will have some idea of the odour which assailed the nostrils of the luckless sergeant who had the unenviable task of awakening the room at 01.00 hrs.

The chaos of the previous night was nothing to the mayhem which followed his wakening call!

Imagine, if you can, four hundred men, all climbing out of rickety and very unstable camp beds, with eighteen inches of space to dress in, most in the latter stages of sleep and the effects of beer, trying to balance on one leg to get trousers on, bursting for a pee or feeling the ominous thunderings of the previous evening's curry, and all attempting to get to either the wash basins or the toilets at the same time.

It says something for the lads there, that not one scene of violence broke out or a single fist was thrown in anger during the whole period they were ensconced in that terrible situation. On the contrary, the atmosphere, apart from that created by beer, curry, mushy peas and old socks, was one of hilarity for the duration. As one officer later put it, 'It was so bloody awful, you had to laugh!' Not that the sergeants, inspectors and even a couple of chief inspectors were let off lightly. No, they were put in a wooden hut! Albeit next to the mess hall, but lacking the creature comforts of thick walls, a heating system, and the marginal, if doubtful, advantage of having the combined heat of four hundred men in close confinement. *And* they had to use the same five wash basins and four toilets! They had all sacrificed a blanket apiece to cover windows and doors, to stop the howling gales rattling through. And it must be borne in mind that there was a frost for every night they were in these huts, which dropped the air temperature down to minus five!

The enduring memory which seems to be embedded in the minds of most of the men involved, was the one of hysterical hilarity they experienced as they were finally leaving. Just as the last transit roared out of the main gate, there, in the final stages of erection, the water just being turned on, was a huge Portaloo!

During the miners' strike it became necessary for police officers from various forces to be deployed for the purposes of patrolling housing estates in many of the coalfield areas.

I was in with a good crew, and we were patrolling about six villages in Yorkshire. Being dropped off two at a time to walk round territory which we did not know protecting people we had never met from those we didn't recognize, and all at three o'clock in the morning in invariably freezing cold and wet weather conditions. Malc and I were dropped off in a small mining village and with collars drawn up to the chin, scarves wrapped tightly round throats, and helmets pulled down over our eyes as protection from the wind, we wandered around looking for people on foot to stop and check. All were apparently safely tucked up in bed, and we were both cold and miserable as we made our way back to the pickup point.

It was four o'clock in the morning, and there, on the footpath in front of us, stood a dear little old lady. Flora hat, old black coat which reached her ankles, and a large black bag.

'Good morning,' says I. She backed off slowly, eyes ever watchful.

'Good morning,' says Malc. Her rearward movement took on greater urgency.

'Are you alright, dear?' I asked kindly.

'Can we help you?' Malc asked, even more kindly.

'I'm waiting for my father and my older brother,' the ld lady stated. 'They've gone out drinking and left me) wait here. They're always doing that!'

Malc and I stared at her. Waiting for her father? Good rief, she was ninety if she was a day.

'Where do you live, love?' Malc asked in his softest ancashire drawl.

'Oh, just over there,' she pointed with quavery hand a the general direction of a row of houses opposite us.

'We'll walk you home, love,' says I, and between us e escorted her over the road, looking at each other ver the top of her bobbing floral hat.

'I don't really need this escort,' says the old girl, 'you on't, y'know, not when you're a qualified air-raid arden and aircraft observer.' We nodded in agreement!

Reaching the sanctuary of the other side of the road, he made off with determined tread towards the rear of ne of the houses.

'Down here,' she states, pointing at a dark passage etween houses. 'It used to be a farm. The road's full of otholes and mud, so be careful.' Sure enough, she was ght, and with a soggy 'gloop' sound, my boot dropped ato a huge puddle and wet seeped in over the top. I ursed under my breath, and Malc, being a true com- ade in arms, tried desperately not to laugh. It came out ke a strangled 'MMmmmmmm!' I glared at him.

We came to a back door, and the old lady staggered a it as she groped in her handbag.

'Oh,' she says, 'I don't think I can get the key in the)ck.'

'Give it to me, love,' I says, and hold out my hand)wards her.

With great deliberation, her little clenched fist came ver my open hand, and with equal slowness it opened) deposit into my waiting palm – nothing! Not a thing! 1alc was turned away, his hand over his mouth as he

choked and spluttered. I stared in amazement at he
little smiling face turned up to look at me.

I made a frantic effort of unlocking the back door wit
an invisible key, doing a great imitation of clicks an
rattles in my throat to simulate a key going in. To ou
amazement, the back door opened and in she went. Sh
reached up for the light switch and found it first time
walked over to the sink and proceeded to fill her kettl
from the tap.

'Put the keys on the draining board, young man,' sh
says! Exit Malc in the last stages of hysteria and all se
control gone. I hear his 'Hahahahahahahaha!' echoin
around the farmyard as I frantically look around th
kitchen for a sign of the elusive keys. Nothing!

Playing it off the cuff, so to speak, I placed th
invisible keys down on the draining board. Her bird
like eyes look down.

'There's nothing there!' she states in a determine
voice.

I look blankly down at her.

'You've lost them! Oh well, can't be helped,' and sh
proceeds to pour out a cup of tea.

I back out of the door, mind racing. My last view i
one of her sitting down in a high-backed chair, facin
the roaring gas fire, head nodding as she hummed an
sipped her tea.

Closing the door, I race back out of the yard to wher
Malc is leaning weakly on a wall, tears running down hi
face! Looking wildly over our shoulders, we run dow
the road to the pickup point, and as the transit pulls up
dive headlong into the rear, shouting for the driver t
get us away from this madhouse!

We learned some time later, that the local bobby ha
been called out from his hard-earned slumbers at five
thirty to attend a domestic in his village, when an ol
lady was found by a householder sitting in his kitchen

warming herself in front of his fire, drinking his tea and eating his biscuits after making herself a substantial meal of eggs and bacon, and refusing to leave because she had been told to stay there by the police!!

10

Strike a Happy Medium

I have always tended to make a comparison between the County, or rural, forces and the larger Metropolitan forces. Perhaps it is because being in the former, I make this comparison with a slightly jaundiced eye. To most large urban forces, we in the country are the 'woolly-backs', and as such we suffer greatly at any gathering from comments about our sexual prowess with sheep, and undignified leg-pulling with regard to our use of wellies worn in bed. On the other hand, it is refreshing to see a transferee from a Metropolitan force trying to come to grips with the all-out coppering done in the wilds. Firstly, we 'woollybacks' tend to have areas far larger than those in the towns. One of my colleagues has a beat which stretches from Richmond in Yorkshire, right across to the west coast, an over-all 'beat' of over sixty square miles. This is bigger than some Metropolitan Police areas! Secondly, we have to do almost everything that comes up by ourselves. It's no good asking for a traffic mobile to come and deal with an accident when the nearest 'jam-buttie' is possibly thirty miles away. You are your own coroner's officer, Disease of Animals inspector, and generally do your own CID and crime prevention work. You also learn very quickly how to talk your way out of trouble! It could take the nearest assistance some twenty minutes to get to you in the case of a fight.

So, when it came about some years ago that we were

called in as back-up for the steel dispute, I saw this comparison very clearly. The difference showed right from the start! Beginning with the bus. A tired, very dilapidated and out-of-date charabanc of doubtful vintage, it creaked and groaned its way towards Sheffield in a pall of black smoke.

Huge convoys of other buses swept past us, led by immaculate police out-riders on motor cycles, and from behind our hands we shamefacedly watched bobbies in shirt-sleeves reclining in high-backed seats watching videos, all to be followed by two more motorcyclists and a patrol car with blue lights on. We, meanwhile, rattled and shuddered our way towards the meeting point.

Our chagrin was heightened when we arrived late, and were directed by a very aloof inspector into a parking space tucked out of sight behind a large brick wall. On the order to 'de-bus', there was a wild scramble to get off, which caused the aloof inspector's nose to wrinkle even more. After all, there was a 'procedure' to be adopted when getting off or getting on to a bus, and our wild-eyed exodus was *not* the one stipulated. But then, he hadn't been sitting on hard seats for about five hours, having been brought in at short notice from the various pubs and clubs off-duty policemen attend when off duty, then subjected to a body-jarring ride on roads flooded with rain. He merely saw thirty or more bobbies frantically trying to get off the bus and trying to undo zipped and buttoned flies at the same time. The wall upon which our charabanc leaned was soon rattling to the gurgle of umpteen gallons of reconstituted beer and spirits! The nose wrinkled up and out of sight. It was no good him trying to complain to our boss, because he too was leaning with his forehead against the wall in relief as his contribution swept the dust away from the scene.

We were directed, from a distance, I noted, by a wave of a well-manicured hand, to a large door set into the Police Headquarters. We duly trooped in, and stood in amazement at the sight which greeted our eyes.

An enormous room, high-ceilinged and ornate with cherubs and nude plaster women, was filled to capacity with bobbies. Hundreds of them! All circulating like blue planets around their various sergeants and inspectors. Order and tranquillity were the obvious essence of the gathering. We were informed by a well-groomed sergeant that briefing was to be in one hour, and on hearing this the inspector in charge of us turned to speak with his Unit. Only it wasn't there! There was a small whirlpool of dust, but no bodies. Having been told that there was an hour to go, the entire Support Unit was gone! The inspector looked blankly round at his three sergeants, who were also trying to surreptitiously walk backwards out of the light.

'Find them. You have an hour.' The boss looked weakly around him, then sat down heavily in a chair, praying that a senior officer did not ask him who he was, and where was his Unit.

I had been slightly slow in getting away, but followed in the disappearing wake of the scruffy blue mass that thundered down large corridors. Suddenly I was alone, and lost. Deep in the bowels of some huge warren of rank and order and unknown rooms.

I listened carefully. Ah! There it was. The tell-tale vowels of a Dalesman. I opened a door and peered in. Seated on a desk, and sipping a large pot of tea I saw one of my colleagues. At his feet, and searching for biscuits, was a very attractive policewoman.

'Now then, Chip. Does tha' want a pot o' tea. Yon little lassie had just brewed. Theer's biscuits anall.'

'Thanks Dick. Not cramping your style, am I?'

'Nay lad. Not brought me wellies, have I?'

'Seen any of the other lads?'

'Aye. Some's gone into a canteen for a jar. Some's

gone to play snooker, and some's gone to find some-wheres to kip down.'

I accepted the tea from the pretty WPC with thanks.

After a while, we left the warmth and comfort of the room, and entered the corridor in time to bump into ten or so of our colleagues.

'Now then, Chip. Now then, Dick. Where's t'room wi inspector innit?'

'Don't know lad. But yon cooms an inspector of sorts. Thoo can ask him.'

Dick pointed with a gnarled finger at an approaching bevvy of 'brass'. (Sheep dipping and bailer twine binding does gnarl the fingers, mind.) One of the lads walked up to the ensemble of Very High Ranking Officers, and flapped a casual finger up to a hatless forehead in salute.

'Now then, boss. If you're goin' to the big room with all those bairns and birds on the roof, can we tag along anall?'

The VHRO went a shade purple, and I did think that his aide de camp was going to faint. The trouble with rural forces is that one only sees the Chief Inspector for a rollocking or assessment once a year. Superintendents tend to wear tweed suits and hats with fishing flies in, and the Chief Constable appears in a fading photograph on the crew-room wall. I mind the time that one of my Chief Constables called at my rural beat house on a Sunday; he was passing so he thought he would call in, and I opened the door to see a small dapperly dressed man standing on my doorstep, smiling. I thought he looked a bit familiar, but couldn't think where I had seen him. Anyway, I was off duty, had some friends in for dinner, and we were all drunk on home-brew. So I assumed he was an insurance salesman, and told him politely to 'sod off and come back Monday'. It wasn't until I saw him walk dejectedly back to his official green Jaguar, and his uniformed driver leaning on the roof with shoulders shaking that I realized my mistake! Anyway, I digress.

So, to my colleague, the VHRO must be a Chief Inspector, because he was in uniform and had silver braid on his hat. That was not normal, but in the big forces, even inspectors have silver braid on their peaks.

Still the embarrassing chatter went on, as Dennis walked chummily alongside the senior rank, answering all his questions with chirpy good humour and down to earth statements. A lesser VHRO pointed a brown-gloved hand towards two huge doors, and with a wave to his new mate, Dennis indicated with sweeping arm movement, à la US cavalry, towards the exit. We trooped through, and found ourselves standing not far away from our dejected boss and his sergeants three. His face lit up, and we crowded round his table, as he ticked our names off his board. All present and accounted for. With two minutes to spare.

'Better button up your tunics, lads. Oh, and put ties on. They can be funny here about the dress and appearance.'

'Oh, I don't know, boss,' Dennis countered, desperately looking in all his pockets for his tie, 'the Chief Inspector we saw didn't mention anything amiss.'

The boss blanched a bit around the gills.

'Chief Inspector? What Chief Inspector?'

'That 'un', stated Dennis, as the entire room rose to greet the Chief Constable of our host force. All rose, that is, except the boss. He remained seated with his face buried in his hands.

Mind you, this *esprit de corps* and natural manner does work in a great many cases where a less individualistic force has had difficulty. I am in no way denigrating my colleagues from the City and Metropolitan forces. They have my, and my colleagues', undying respect for the job they do under the most terrific pressures. In my neck of the woods, the local bobby does, to some extent, still rate as someone 'special' in the community. On a par with the vicar and the schoolmaster. In the cities it is a different story. Respect has gone out the window, it seems, and some of the bobbies find it hard to remain calm and polite when abused verbally, spat at, and generally ignored for the jobs they have to do.

I recall in the Toxteth riots seeing a police car pull up in the lee of a large block of flats. The crew got out to assist in searching for youths who had been petrol bombing and looting shops, and were only just clear when a fridge and a television set hurtled down to smash on to the roof and bonnet of the Panda. Now *you* try being polite and understanding when something like that happens to you.

It is in the individual approach to people that perhaps we have the edge on our hard-working colleagues in the city. When I had my beat out in the sticks, I knew every one of our parishioners. Mind you, I only had a small beat, about twenty-two square miles and four thousand souls on the voters' register. I felt this most acutely during the miners' strike, that saddest of affairs.

We were on duty at one of the 'open mines'; that is, one which doesn't have a cage and lift, but a gradual shaft which dips slowly underground. Construction on this particular mine wasn't even finished, but we had to go and make sure the construction workers weren't harassed in any way.

We were on site by three A.M., and parked up with the kettle boiling two minutes later, watching for first light to continue our game of cricket on the road leading to the pit.

The 'night shift' of pickets were sitting around their fire, and as was our usual manner, two of us went over to share cigarettes, tobacco and the inimitable 'Max-pax'. (These are plastic cups with a covering of powdered tea, coffee, or chocolate in the bottom. Just add hot water, and Presto!, a hot drink.) They, in turn, would pile more wood on the brazier, and we would chat about the general situation until their relief came. They would tell us how many pickets were expected that morning, and we would tell the boss who would inform the control room. All very sensible and dignified. If there was to be a big attendance for whatever reason at another pit, then we could relax and enjoy the day out; they could get on with their odd shout of 'scab' as the contractors went in.

If there *was* going to be a bit of a 'do' on at our pit, then we made sure that our contingent was 'in charge' of 'our' pickets. This way, no one got hurt on either side, none of our pickets got locked up, and when it was all over we resumed a normal way of life. It does sound idyllic, I know, but there were times when my support unit were right in the thick of it. I saw acts of gross stupidity from both sides, but even in the midst of 'battle', there was always at least one friendly face in the opposing crowd when you looked.

I recall the time at another pit, we had adopted our practice of 'scratching each other's backs', when the bus containing the working miners came into view. Our opposite numbers put out their shared fags, and apologized to us but, as they explained, the TV cameras were there, and if they were caught fraternizing or not pushing and shouting, they would be in trouble with the Union. So we linked arms, and after assuring the miners that we were comfortable, they heaved and swelled at our ranks, shouting and screaming like men demented, fists shaking and abusing the bus as it went past.

During the heaving, my mate's helmet got displaced, and slid over his eyes, the chin strap sliding under his throat and threatening to strangle him. I was touched to see the loudest-shouting and angriest-faced miner in the crowd quietly reach up out of sight and release my mate's chinstrap. Later that night, I saw the incident on the TV news, and there we all were, to all intents and purposes on opposite sides and fighting all the way. Frightening, really. People just didn't realize then, nor later, that in the main there was more cordiality between police and miners than was ever portrayed by the media. My two fondest memories of the whole dispute were at the pit affectionately known at 'Big K', and later at 'our' pit near Selby.

In the first incident, we knew that we were in for a 'big 'un', as by five-thirty in the morning there were over five hundred cars parked on the roads leading to the pit. Allowing three pickets per car, we knew we were in for a pounding. When it started, we were forced to hide behind colleagues with shields, as bricks and cobbles, paving stones and lumps of wood came whistling over. I don't know about anyone else, but I was in danger of needing clean underwear within a few minutes. More police rolled up, then even more, as we in ordinary helmets were slowly retreating from the firing line. Then one of our bosses got up on a wall with a megaphone.

'You men will cease this violence immediately!' he roared, and my low opinion of any rank above sergeant soared dramatically. It was a very brave thing to do, and such was the impact he made, that the mayhem did, in fact, cease.

'If you insist on continuing this barrage, then I shall bring more policemen here, then more, and even more, until you are outnumbered and quelled. Do you understand?' The metallic voice boomed over our heads. There was a muted rumble from the miners assembled in front of us. The situation was very tense. Then a voice piped up from the men on the picket line.

'If you do that, and bring up more policemen, you know what I'll do?'

'You'll do what?!' the metallic voice boomed back in defiance. We waited with bated breath.

103

'I'll tell my big brother, that's what!' came back the reply, and the whole ensemble erupted into hysterical laughter. And the TV crews left the scene with nothing further to record, heads down in apparent dejection.

The second occasion which sticks firmly and fondly in my mind was the Christmas before the lads went back to work. It was freezing cold, and we had arrived very early. Tubes of Max-pax were broken out, and transported across to the pickets' little hut. To our surprise and delight, the 'lads' were in fancy dress, Father Christmas, Sir Walter Raleigh, a snowman. Marvellous! The next thing I knew was our inspector getting us all together, and with artificial snow being sprayed liberally about from a can, we stood in the firelight's flicker and sang Christmas carols as the Press filmed and snapped in amazement. Later that day, we were sent further down into the mining area, where I ended up arresting a youth on a spiteful picket line where violence ruined the happy picture. What was worse, the young chap wasn't even a miner. He was a student.

An amusing finale to the whole episode was told to me by a colleague in a large force outside Yorkshire. A character who became famous to us bobbies was a picket who I don't think ever actually went on the picket lines. Instead, he would make his vigil on the lawn outside his house. Dressed in trousers and vest, carpet slippers on his feet, he stood in defiant magnificence holding a placard which read 'five months out and still fighting', then 'six months out', 'ten months out', and so on. He would spend about ten minutes a day shouting abuse at the lines of transits going past his front lawn, in fair weather or foul, his fist shaking at the convoys as they left the area.

Always his anger and shouted abuse was far worse to those who were dressed in white shirts, usually indicating a Metropolitan Force, whose reputations were quite over-exaggerated. (I think!) Anyway, it was on the last day of the strike, and for the last time we drove past this magnificent little man in his rabbit-like defiance. A last wave, which seemed to drive him to the point of apoplexy, and he was gone from our sight.

Later a contingent of our colleagues came past. They had been on the receiving end of his abuse every day, and today was the last day. It transpired that they stopped outside his house.

He was found later on a motorway bridge on the M62, complete with placard, trousers, vest and carpet slippers, unhurt but very angry! But I'm sure it didn't really happen!

11

Forever in the Dark

Three funny little incidents I heard of are now recalled,
all involving officers on night shifts. As stated previously,
a night shift, especially the first one after 'days off', is
really very debilitating. At about three in the morning,
sleep sweeps over you, and you would sell your grand-
mother to just put your head down and doze for even a
few minutes. It can get so bad that you can even
hallucinate! No kidding. I know officers who have seen
something peculiar through sleep-fogged eyes, and
dashed up to a house with every intent of arresting what
appears to be a very suspiciously acting conifer trying
the front window!

Such was the case for a colleague in a northern seaside
resort. It was, to be fair, his very first night shift out on
his own.

He patrolled his lock-up property with diligence and
conscientious door and window rattling. Second half,
and his eyes were beginning to droop as he plodded his
way tiredly round the harbourside towards the amusement arcade. Something caught his eye, and glancing
up, he saw a man standing on the cliffs overlooking the
town. Arms out and legs akimbo, the man stood in stark
outline against the night sky, ready to launch himself
out into oblivion and the road surface below.

'Oh my God!' the worthy young man stood and
assessed the situation. Fumbling with his radio, he
stated that he had a potential suicide on the cliffs, gave

the location and probable point of impact, then dispensing with his PR, started to run up the road.

The man appeared to be undecided as to his actual time of launch into space, but swayed from side to side as the young officer ran as hard as he could towards the cliffs.

'Stay where you are!' he shouted as he ran pell mell towards the hill leading up to the steps which in turn led to the man. He was still there!

'Don't do it! This is the police. Stand still. I'm coming to help you,' his voice rasped hysterically. Dear God, don't let him jump as I'm halfway up to stop him, he prayed.

Still shouting at the top of his voice, he ran up the steps, almost sheer in ascent, aware that below him the sergeant and the other members of the shift were making desperate attempts to get to help him.

Arriving at the top, he skidded round the ornamental gardens and dashed to the spot where he had seen the man. Gone! Oh dear Lord, no. Too late!

He peered nervously over the lip of the cliff. Nothing!

Glancing wildly around him, he looked in desperation for the sight of a dejected looking fellow trudging away from his location. Again, nothing.

As the blue lights on the GP car rounded the corner, and his colleagues bounded with gasping and wheezing breath up the steps towards him, he looked up and saw the figure of Captain Cook, arms astretch, legs akimbo, standing on his plinth overlooking the harbour!

Another colleague, again young in service, recalled to me an event which was not only embarrassing, but again emphasizes the strain 'nights' put on an officer. He was also in a northern town, and his beat took in a large and opulent shopping precinct.

Wearily, he made his way around the brightly-lit arcade, peering myopically through tired eyes at the various windows and trying the all too secure doors. His mind was screaming out for sleep! The kids had woken just as he came in at seven A.M. after his previous night shift, and continued to shout and play with their friends with all the exuberance of four year olds. Result, broken and most unsatisfying sleep until about eleven o'clock. Then he had been forced to just get up.

He looked with envy at the small benches set into recesses in the arcade, and with a glance at his watch, walked wearily across to the nearest and most convenient one situated behind a rustic display of climbing plants. Seating himself into the recess, and drawing his legs up with arms wrapped round knees, like a helmeted 'Joan the Wad', he allowed his helmet to slip over his eyes and sighed. Just a few minutes' rest, that's all he needed, he told himself.

He was awakened by the sound of giggling and, opening one bleary eye, saw two small children observing him with wide-eyed, thumb-in-mouth wonderment. He was aware of a hustle and bustle of people going about their daily business, and leaped out of his alcove with a panic-stricken look at his watch. Ten-thirty in the morning!! He walked dejectedly towards the police station and the rollicking which was sure to follow!

Driving during the winter months on night patrol is surely the most cruel form of 'night starvation' ever invented. Into the warm car, patrol, out of the warm car, do property, into the warm car . . . The desire to let your head drop is foremost, and the act of turning off the heater is not even considered.

The old minivans were dreadful for the winter shifts. The heaters were on permanent blow from the fan. The fan in turn set up a constant and mind numbing noise which, coupled with its heat, had the eyes rolling backwards into the head within a few miles of driving. The body slumped further and further down the seat,

nd only the radio kept you awake. During the early
ours, even the radio went quiet, and that was murder!
A good friend of mine suffered unlimited agonies as a
esult of this.

It was a freezing February night, and he had been
riving around the areas of the countryside covering not
nly his own beat, but that of two colleagues who were
n leave and 'days' respectively. The wind was howling,
he outside temperature was four or five below freezing,
he roads were very dodgy and requiring all his bug-
yed concentration, and his head was beginning to
evelop the 'nodding dog' syndrome! Eyeballs covered
vith sandpaper, and refusing to focus at anything further
han the edge of the bonnet, he felt the van clip the
erge. Enough is enough, he thought. Time to pull over
nd get himself sorted out. Have a walk or a smoke. Do
omething to waken himself up!

He pulled into a lay-by, and switched off the engine.
Vith the engine stilled, so too was the fan on the heater.
After a minute or two, he noted the condensation
ppearing on the windscreen. His head nodded again,
nd he pulled his collar up around his neck in an effort
o keep out the encroaching cold.

'Must waken up,' he told himself as his eyelids
umbled downwards and his neck jerked him into
udden upright position. Then his eyelids drooped again
nd his head lolled against the window.

He snapped back awake as the radio urgently called
is callsign. He brought his wrist up to his eyes and
ooked at his watch in the gloom, his head still resting
n the window. God, it was cold! Hell's teeth, he had
een asleep for twenty minutes! He reached over for
he handset, and nearly pulled his head off his shoulders!
His head was stuck to the glass! The complete side
vindow was covered in ice on the inside, and frozen
nto it, his hair! The radio crackled again, more urgently,
nd he struggled to pull himself free. No good! He had

no alternative but to kick the handset off its clamp, and wrap his legs around the coiled wire, drawing it towards him until his outstretched hand grasped the cable. Head still fastened to the window, he answered their call. An accident about six miles away, could he attend? He shouted the affirmative, and threw the handset to the passenger seat within hand's grab. Then he managed to start the van, looking out of the one eye which looked forward!

Four miles he travelled, looking forward with one eye on the road! His thick hair was still splayed out and stuck firmly to the side window. Slowly, slowly he monitored the creeping dampness spread along the windscreen, and move with frustrating slowness along the window towards his head. Finally, and with a brain-crackling ripping sound, he felt his head resume its normal position on his shoulders.

Arriving at the scene, he saw it was a single vehicle, with no injuries, just a very shaken driver looking at a very bent Ford Escort.

The driver got into his van as he pulled up, and looked at him through red-rimmed eyes.

'I fell asleep,' he stated.

'Easy done,' the officer said sympathetically!

12

Christmas Crackers

Christmas is a time of rejoicing, of peace, of goodwill to all men. So we are told! For three days of the year, you would think that a bobby could walk the beat or patrol in area in the confident hope that he would be unbothered or unfettered by crimes or domestics. Nooo way!

One Christmas I was doing a late patrol around my beat, and covering the beat adjoining mine as the officer concerned was off and enjoying the Christmas festivities. Christmas Night, with a sharp frost to keep the punters indoors watching the late-night film. Already the minivan windows refused to open, frozen solid. The passenger-door was also stuck, as the ice gripped the rubber to the metal.

I turned into the large car park of the service station on the A1, with the intention of calling in and wishing them all a Merry Christmas over a hot coffee. But it was in total darkness! Then I remembered, Christmas Day was the only day in the year the place closed down entirely. Sighing, I glanced at my watch, and was about to pull out on to the road again, when a very large lorry drove into the car park and stopped over in the far corner. Suspicious?

I turned off my sidelights, and quietly motored over to the wagon, swinging the van round such that my window, which was also frozen closed, was looking up at the driver's cab door. I shone my torch. The door flew open, and in so doing completely demolished the 'Police'

111

sign and blue light on top of the van. The van rocked a
umpteen pairs of Doc Martins thumped over the roo
using it as a springboard to safety and escape. They wer
never ending! The radio aerial followed its blue-glasse
neighbour, and the roof slowly began to sink dow
towards me! I was gibbering on the radio, only to hea
the strains of 'Noel, noel, noel, noelll!' coming faintl
from the control room staff as they wished all thei
listeners the compliments of the season! I selected first
and drove away from the side of the wagon, to enabl
me to actually get out of my cab and make pursuit o
what was about eighteen youths who had all bee
ensconced in the wagon cab!

I heard a yell, and one body flew off the roof on to th
ground behind me. Another slid backside first down th
windscreen, taking the wiper blades with him. I stoppe
and got out, as the youth bounced down the bonne
with sufficient force to place a large, buttock-sized den
in the middle. His colleague was limping away, and
grabbed the two of them. On went the handcuffs, and
escorted them to the rear of the van.

'Get in,' I ordered, and they dutifully opened the tw
rear doors for access, ripping the large expanse of rubbe
off the seal on the double doors.

'Er, sorry, constable,' they murmured, trying to fin
something to do with the writhing rubber ring they no
found in their hands.

The rear doors wouldn't shut, of course due to th
roof being bowed in the middle, so I walked them roun
to the front. I think I must have lost my power of reason
because I gestured to them to get into the front seat an
clamber over the seat to the back. They both looke
blankly at the second large writhing ring of rubbe
which had come their way from opening the passenge
door.

'Sod it!' I said with venom, and took them round t
the driver's door, which I opened and with deft sleigh

112

of hand re-cuffed them with the steering wheel being used as a centre anchor.

The control room had finished their Yuletide serenading, and answered my call. What men were available turned up at the scene, and stared in amazement at the remnants of my minivan! The two men were grabbed by two burly traffic officers, and escorted with some force towards a large traffic car. But only after the van steering wheel was drawn with some force over towards the open door! I stood looking at my little van. I had pulled on to the forecourt at eleven fifteen. The time was now eleven forty-five. In half an hour, the van was a wreck. I looked round. Everyone had gone, to look for the other elusive runners. Over the radio, I heard 'Silent Night, Hooly . . .' and sat down dejectedly on the remnants of the van bonnet!

A colleague of mine was on Christmas duty one evening, sitting in the police station doing some report writing. About eleven thirty in the evening, just as he was preparing to go out, there was a loud hammering on the front doors.

Opening the door, he was confronted by a woman, very heavily pregnant, and a very wild-eyed man! The man gibbered about his car breaking down, and paced up and down shouting to the clear skies above, 'Why does this sort of thing only happen to me?' The woman, on the other hand, leaned against the solid pillars of the front porch, panting and calmly concentrating on her obvious contractions!

The local hospital was some eight miles away, and my colleague realized that the woman was very close, and that her husband was going to be useless!

He brought the couple into the police station, and made the woman comfortable in a large, soft chair. Then he phoned for a doctor, and an ambulance. The doctor was on call, and the ambulance was attending the results

of a pub fight which required its immediate attention.
Christmas has this effect on people who go out to enjoy
themselves! So he was left with one alternative. To take
the woman to the hospital himself in a police car.

The woman's contractions were coming every fifteen
minutes, and she was coping well with the situation. It
would take fifteen minutes' fast driving to get to the
hospital, so he outlined his idea to the mother-to-be.
(The father was in a state of total uselessness!)

When the next contraction finished, they all got up
and went to the police car, the woman in the back seat,
feet up, and the father in the front, belted up!

They were halfway to the hospital, when the woman
mentioned with her unshakeable calmness that her
waters had broken, and so my colleague put his foot
down. Just out of town, he radioed for assistance and
asked for the hospital to be informed of the impending
birth, then stopped short. The woman was in advanced
labour, and he turned to the husband for assistance or
help in some way. The would-be father gave a long sigh
– and fainted! With pounding heart, my colleague undid
the man's safety belt, and loosened his collar and belt,
then struggled to get him out on to the verge for fresh
air.

Tipping the front seats forward, he then set about
coping with the birth. His first disadvantage was that he
only had a rudimentary idea of what was supposed to
happen. He was single, young and not too *au fait* with
the internal gubbins of pregnant women! However, the
woman seemed to have supreme confidence in his
ability, saying how calm he made her feel, and with this
to live up to, he 'plodded on'. The second disadvantage
was that he had no torch, and his car had one of those
internal lights which is set above the windscreen. Subsequently, when he knelt in front of the woman, he was
looking at his own shadow! The woman then mentioned
that she had a little torch in her handbag, on a key-ring,

114

and when he found it he began to look into the problem in a new light, so to speak.

The birth went ahead with surprising ease, and he recalled that the placenta was not to be detached from the baby, but wrapped up with it in a complete bundle. He had removed his jacket for the operation, and had used this to cover the girl's top half. The baby could not be wrapped up in the blanket which was part of the car's equipment, as it was too grubby. So off came his shirt! Clean on at ten, he reminded himself. Out came the baby and, as if to protest at its ignominious beginnings, it started to bawl as it hit the back seat. All the other 'bits' followed, and were wrapped up in his shirt, complete with babe, and the whole parcel handed to the proud and tired mother.

He relayed the good news to the control room, who informed him that the ambulance was on the way, along with a back-up police car. As he returned the handset to the rest, the ambulance turned up with its attendant car. He got out, and looked at the husband who was slowly getting up. He turned to the policeman with a silly, self-conscious look on his face, and my colleague told him he was a father, it was a girl, and mother and daughter were doing fine. The man nodded, and his trousers fell down around his ankles as he slumped on to the verge again!

My colleague married soon afterwards, and I remember when his wife had their first little boy. For all his confidence 'under fire' and his self assurance in dealing with a humorous and touching moment at the roadside, he appeared at my front door to announce the birth with a large bottle of Johnny Walker in his hand and a sideways grin on his face which was surmounted by a pair of boggling eyes!

'I'm a Dad,' he announced, and held out the bottle which, when it was safely in my hands, gave him the freedom to collapse in a dead faint on my hall carpet!

115

13

Poetic Justice

Never work with children or animals. Isn't that wha[t]
they say in the theatre? Well, the same applies in th[e]
force. Animals are a constant source of not only amuse[-]
ment, but heart-ache to most coppers. They are s[o]
unpredictable. (See Pig, Training College, Horses an[d]
Civil Disputes training!)

Many anecdotes are forthcoming on this subject, no[t]
least the one which purports to be about the WPC wh[o]
attended her first Traffic Accident to find that it ha[d]
involved a horse in collision with a car. The car wa[s]
severely damaged, and its occupants badly shocked, bu[t]
the horse had been killed by the impact.

Dealing admirably with the gory business, getting the
driver and passengers away to hospital, she requested
the attendance of someone who could move the horse'[s]
carcass. Once the road was clear, and the carcass
removed, she then returned to the police station to
write up her report and clear the logs. The immorta[l]
words were then transcribed for all to see and for
posterity . . .

'I attended scene. Single vehicle only, in collision
with horse. Injuries to car passengers slight, but taken
to hospital. Horse unfortunately killed by impact. Car
removed from scene by B's garage. Horse towed away
by the knackers!' Marvellous!

In a similar vein another of my colleagues, a country-
man born and bred, was instructed to go to a local
doctor's house. A complaint had been received from the

good doctor to the effect that his front garden had been invaded by a herd of cows, which were causing some damage. This being half-past one in the morning, the bobby knows that to trace the ownership of the cows will be impossible. Nonetheless, he attends the scene. Sure enough, there is the doctor standing in his front garden, flapping limply at a herd of boisterous young bullocks who were eating his prize floribunda and hybrid teas.

The bobby, with suitable language and a very large stick, drove them skilfully out of the garden, down the road and into a field which he knew was 'laid to fallow', as the rural folk have it. Having placed them in this field, he returned to get details of the damage and complete his report.

Impish humour being what it is, he could not resist putting the following on the logs for all to see . . .

'Attended scene. These are *not* cows, but bullocks. Suffice it to say I removed Doctor F's bullocks painlessly and placed them in a field!'

It does make for a laugh in those duller moments of life.

Another incident which lends weight to the warning at the beginning of this chapter relates to a crew on nights in the Manchester area. They were attending a call regarding a pack of dogs on a housing estate.

Pulling up outside the complainant's house in the early hours of the morning, they heard much snarling and snapping coming from the rear of the premises. The old lady who had phoned gesticulated from out of her upstairs window, and pointed to the cobbled alley which ran between the 'back to back' terraces.

The two officers ran round the back, and were confronted by the sight of about ten or fifteen dogs, all surrounding 'something', and attacking it with vigour. Striding into the pack with staffs flying, the intrepid duo

117

drove them off, and found themselves to be face to face with – an alligator! Oh, it was quite a small alligator, as alligators go. But, in Manchester, you don't usually see them on the streets.

Backing off hastily, yet retaining that element of dignity which surrounds all policemen when they are unsure of what to do next, they went to the end of the alley and considered the problem.

They decided that the alligator, which had calmed down considerably since their arrival, and was in the process of demolishing something from a knocked-over dustbin, should be contained. But the situation was delicate in as much that it could cause panic if the general public got to know about it. They could not use their radios to notify the control, as they both knew that certain members of the press tended to monitor police transmissions for freelance purposes.

The alligator was not fully grown, it was about three feet long, but they knew that its teeth, at least, were well developed!

They both plumped for discretion! The large blanket was brought from the boot of the car, and advancing slowly, they held the blanket unfurled. A quick throw, and the alligator was covered in the enveloping folds. With much thrashing and hissing the alligator showed surprising strength as it fought the sudden covering, and the two men were hard put to wrap it up such that it was secure.

Swearing and struggling, they took the thrashing blanket to the boot of the car, deposited it inside and slammed the lid down! Breathing heavily, they then got into the car and drove slowly back to the nick, parking up in the far reaches of the car park.

They then went in to the Duty Sergeant, and explained the situation to him, thereby relieving themselves of all responsibility. He, of course, being a man of resourcefulness, immediately passed it on to the Duty

118

Inspector, who in turn, with shaking finger, dialled the Chief Inspector's extension. No reply.

White in the face, the Inspector tried again, to be informed by the Chief Inspector's duty cadet that the old man was out in the station area somewhere, doing – and here the lad became very conspiratorial – 'special snap checks on vehicles, equipment and general tidyness'.

They dashed down to the car park, in time to see the chief, torch in hand, opening the boot of the Panda which, to him, appeared to be hidden in the darkest recess of the car park only because it was either damaged or was put out of sight for some other sinister reasons.

The boot was opened, and the blanket triumphantly removed with a flourish! A loud hiss, accompanied by a wincing snap of jaws, obviously missing their intended target, and an equally loud and drawn out wail of terror was heard by the four men. Quietly they withdrew back into the station to await the Chief Inspector's arrival.

When he did appear, he was white and very composed. He stalked over to the logs, and with a tight-lipped flurry, flipped the pages over to where the entry was made concerning that vehicle's attendance at a disturbance. As the crew stood grinning at his obvious discomfort, they watched as his lips followed the words written therein . . .

'Attended scene. Disturbance caused by dogs harassing a three-foot alligator, repeat, alligator. This reptile was captured by crew of D-76, and as unable to find owner, and in the concern of public safety, reptile placed in boot of vehicle and transported to Station.

Note This vehicle has been placed at the far end of the car park, away from all vehicle and pedestrian traffic until collected by RSPCA. *Under no circumstances* is this vehicle to be either approached or tampered with unless authorized by the Duty Inspector or the Chief Inspector.'

Turning on his heel, the old man stormed out,

slamming the door behind him, to the accompanying gales of laughter which followed!!

With regard to children, I am reminded of an incident told to me by an older constable, who was recalling the days when the young had a lot of respect for the law and its guardians.

'Never got any lip in those days,' he sat back with closed eyes, 'quick clip round the ear and nothing else said or done. None of these namby pamby do-gooders jumping in with silken words about the kids needing "understanding", or giving people their rights. What they didn't know in those days didn't hurt 'em.' He sipped at his red hot tea and glared at us over his huge hands.

'In fact,' he went on, 'I had a lucky escape because kids had respect and fear of the law. Back in '56, it was. I was under the wing of a senior bobby, who had developed a way of dealing with kids all of his own. Marble in the glove.' He blew the steam off his brew, as we all looked at him with raised eyebrows, 'Marble in the glove? You haven't heard of that? Dear Lord,' he shook his head slowly in bemusement, 'it's come as low as that, has it. Well, the marble in the glove was a ploy used by a lot of policemen for "on the spot" justice. You carried your gloves in your hand, and in the finger of one you put a small marble. Now,' he smiled fondly at the memory, 'when you saw a kid doing something wrong or stupid, you clipped him round the ear with your gloves, so that the marble caught him right on the end of the earhole,' he looked round with relish. 'Blimey, you could warm your hands on a kid's ear after a clip like that. Glowed in the dark, they did. Anyway, this night, I'm on a two to ten shift and on me jack. I saw this kid in a doorway, and saw him put his hand quickly behind his back as I approached. About twelve, he was. I stopped, and saw smoke writhing up his back. "What you got there, lad?" I asked him. "Nuffink, mister," he says. "Show me," says I, and sure enough out comes the lit fag. "Stamp it out, laddie," I says and he duly drops it on the floor and grinds it out. "You won't tell me Dad, will you, sir?" he whimpers. "Not I, son, not if you don't." So, he's about to walk off out the doorway, when I remember me marble in the glove. He sees me lift them out from behind me, and makes a break for it, probably had that sort of medicine before. I takes a swipe at him, and catch him a beauty on the ear. However, the force of it splits the finger, and the marble flies out and hits a plate glass window! There's this long, loud crash which seems to go on for ever! The kid's off, and so am I, matching him stride for stride. When he gets round a suitable corner, out of breath and knackered, the kid looks up at me and says: "I won't say nuffink if you don't mister." I just nod, and he's off! Now, that wouldn't happen today now, would it?'

We all nod in agreement, glumly.

Malcolm pours another mug of tea, and munches reflectively on a corned beef sandwich.

'That's true,' he muses, 'that's very true. Take today, for instance. I'm on duty in the town, standing near to the Gents in the Market Place. Along comes this little kid, about seven or eight, eating an ice cream and holding his Mum's hand. Sullen little sod, he looks too. Anyway, his Mum looks a bit bewildered at the traffic, so I decide to see them across the road. Out into the middle I go, and hold up my hand.

'As they walk past, I look at this kid, see, and smiling, I says to him, "Give us a lick of your ice cream, then."

'"Piss off!" he says, and to add to my surprise, kicks me a sharp rap on the shins! Just like that. There I am, hopping on one leg, holding up the traffic as he and his mother continue over the road without a word of thanks!'

'There you are,' says the old constable, 'wouldn't have happened in my day!'

14

High Rises

The lowest rank in the police force is that of constable. The highest rank is also that of constable, albeit Chief Constable. Interspersed between those two titles are ranks of other senior officers. It is similar to working in a very large factory, with different grades of management. In industry, some managers are good, others are bad. Some have got their position through diligence and hard work, others by being in the right place at the right time. Some have a natural talent for leadership, others are totally out of their depth and cover it with a veneer of pomposity. So it is with the police forces throughout the country.

I have been lucky in my career, where, apart from one or two exceptions, I have had senior officers who have left me alone to get on with the job, pulled me up short when I needed it, or helped me out when I turned to them. Not so in other cases I have heard of.

Bandied about is the oft heard cross-talk between a Detective Constable meeting the Chief Superintendent on the stairs. For the purposes of retelling, I have used my own surname to protect the innocent. Chief Supers tend to be austere men, remote from the realities of the job purely because they have not been 'on the streets' for perhaps twenty years. This is not their fault, but due to the demands made on them by the administrative nature of their job. However, it goes something like this . . .

DC. Morning sir.

CS. Ah, morning er, er . . .

DC. Woodhead, sir.

CS. Ah yes, Woodhead. How are you getting on then, Woodman?

DC. Terrible sir. I've just lost a good prisoner who got off on a technicality, I've got behind with me paperwork, and the wife's left me.

CS. Good, good. Glad to hear it, Woodbridge. Wife and children OK are they?

DC. Woodhead sir. No sir, I've just said, she's left me, and we haven't got any kids.

CS. Fine, fine. House all right is it? No complaints?

DC. I'm in digs sir, had to leave my house to pay for the divorce. But it's a grotty dump.

CS. Splendid, splendid. Kids OK at school then?

DC. No sir, I've just said I don't have any.

CS. That's right, quite right, so you did. But apart from that, you're coping with the work. Plenty of traffic offences, eh?

DC. No sir. I'm on CID.

CS. 'Course you are, that's right. Well, carry on Wedgewood. Doing a grand job. Remember me to the wife and family, won't you?

DC. Yes sir, I'll do that when we meet in court. Thank you for listening, sir. I do appreciate it.

CS. Just doing my job, old chap. Always ready to lend an ear. Now, can't stop, off to a meeting. Something about welfare. Well done, lad, keep up the good work, I'm very pleased with your progress. Keep hearing your name all the time. Goodbye, er . . . er . . .

DC. Woodhead, sir.

CS. 'Course it is. Yes well, carry on Woodburn.

DC. Thank you sir. (Exit DC sobbing quietly as he goes upstairs.)

Not true? 'Course it isn't!

The beauty of being in a job such as this is that nearly all the senior ranks have had to come up through the mill, thus they command the very same men who, years previously, they probably walked the beat with. This, of course, does tend to ensure that they think twice before issuing rollickings to junior officers. 'Has this happened to me?' they think. Or, 'Did I do this when it was thrown at me?' or 'How did I act in this type of situation . . .?' If they don't, then a penny to a pinch there's a PC or sergeant on the shift or in the sub-division who remembers *exactly* how he acted and is quite willing to tell him in private!

A young PC was bemoaning the fact that he was up in front of the Chief Inspector that morning, due to his course of actions dealing with a prisoner the previous Saturday night. He had attended a pub fight, and in arresting an extremely violent prisoner had, for his own protection, been forced to give the prisoner a bit of a slap. It had achieved the required result, showing the prisoner he meant business despite his obvious youth-fulness, and that he was taking him in, violent or not. Now he was the subject of an enquiry due to the prisoner's complaint of undue force being used. The lad was obviously worried, and told the sergeant and the rest of the shift so.

The sergeant shifted his position on his chair, and drew out his pipe. Lighting it, and getting it puffing to his satisfaction, he blew a pensive stream of smoke up to the ceiling.

'You do well to worry, lad,' he said to the young officer, 'because assaulting your prisoner, for any reason, is a serious offence not under only the Police Discipline code, but also the Criminal Law. However, I would draw to your attention an incident of similar nature which occurred some fifteen years ago. I was a young PC then, and was in company of a PC a few years older and with a few months more service than me. Walking the beat, we were trying to keep away from trouble and the duty sergeant, which was like one and the same. So, there we are, pounding and rattling door knobs when we are told that there is a pub fight in town. We walk down to the pub, the old Golden Eagle, it's been knocked down now for that new Hintons, but it used to be a real sin bin for the toerags and tealeaves in the manor. Well, we open the door, and it's bedlam! They're all at it, women too, and there's glasses, bottles and fists flying in all directions. My companion gets dropped as we walk in the door, a bottle lands right on his head and down he goes. The barman is shouting on the phone to the nick, then grabs a lump of two by two from under the counter and proceeds to lay about him in no uncertain fashion. I'm hard put to fight my way through to the counter, pulling bodies to right and left and bundling them out into the street. The punch-up is at its height when my oppo comes round. He gets up, and then proceeds to lambaste and banjo everybody he comes into contact with! Fists, boots, he was a one-man power house! He laid out Dave Duggan, the local hard man, with a right hook that would have done justice to "Our 'enery". Dropped him like a sack of tatties. Then his brother follows suit. Well, I just stand back and gape! Not content with that, he then kicks Joey Caffman, a real nasty piece of work, right in the balls so hard it sounded like the Avon lady calling. Well after that, he cleared up the rest with the odd push and shove out of the door. The cavalry arrived and we started to mop up. The Duggan brothers and Caffman were all cuffed together, then taken up to the nick by me and me oppo. Not too gently, neither! They were still kicking and fighting and swearing.

'So, we got 'em locked up, and made out our reports. Next morning, we're brought into work early, about ten o'clock; to face an interrogation from the Chief Inspector. Real tartar, he was, but fair with it. Tells us that we are the subject of a complaint from the Duggans and Caffman for assault and excessive force during last night's arrest. I said nothing, as I had no reason to worry, being only marginally involved. But my opposite number just stood and looked blankly at the boss.

"Who sir, me sir?" he asks, his little face all innocent. "Are you sure they mean me, sir? I *never* use violence. I'm almost pacifist, sir. Mind you, I can't recall what happened last night. I got hit on the head with a bottle by Duggan, and can't remember a thing until I awoke to find myself in bed this morning, sir. In fact, I feel a wee bit dizzy now, if I could sit down a minute please," and holding his head weakly, he sits groggily down.

'Well, what could the boss say? A total blackout during the actual period of the fight, caused by injuries received on duty? Case dismissed.

'Now, lad, I would suggest that you replace that piece of sticking plaster you've got over your left eye with a piece much larger,' the sergeant tapped his pipe out reflectively. 'Then, when you go in to see the boss, you tell him you can't remember a thing about last night. Just say that last night you got a bang on the head, which you did, in fact, and after that you can't remember a thing. I'm sure,' he paused to finish off his dregs of tea, 'I'm sure my old oppo would see your side of the story!'

15

Understatements

Most policemen are blessed with a wry, if not dry humour. Coming up with a classic comment at the most appropriate time. One story I heard was about a journalist driving his very elderly Hillman Minx along the Mall in London. (In those days, journalists were pretty poorly paid.) He sensed that his silencer was beginning to rumble a bit, and as he progressed further, the rumbling grew into a muted roar.

Approaching him came a detachment of the Household Cavalry, harnesses glistening and breastplates twinkling in the watery sunshine. A picture of everything British. As they drew closer, the unfortunate driver was aware that the roar, once muted, was now a cacophony of vibrant noise, as his exhaust pipe gave up its struggle to survive. In a bid to get away from the horses, our journalistic friend swerved into the kerb. However, this course of action merely aggravated the situation by causing the exhaust pipe to become totally detached from the underside of the car, and in an apparent endeavour to commit hara-kiri, it slithered with some velocity across the road in a shower of soot and sparks under the immaculate hooves of the leading horses.

With bellowing exhaust, our writer desperately attempted to drive out of harm's way, as horses reared up, dismounting cursing riders and skittering dangerously close to his car. His attempts to avert disaster simply made matters worse because of the sheer noise coming from the manifold pipes, and along with his powers of reason, his clutch sense went. Leaping forward, he mounted the kerb, and struck a lamp post, to which was attached a very large and very full litter bin. The lamp post stood firm, the litter bin did not, but cast its contents to the prevailing wind, which took it into the seething mass of the prancing and cursing Household Cavalry. The car engine stopped with an explosion like a gunshot, which completely unnerved those steeds not yet affected. And amidst all this chaos, a London bobby watched with impassive eye.

As the noise slowly subsided, the horses stopped leaping and bucking, and their erstwhile riders remounted, the custodian of the law walked with measured and sedate pace towards the luckless and very shaken journalist.

Reaching into his top pocket, and drawing out his notebook, he licked his pencil slowly, then leaning through the open window of the severely bruised Hillman, spoke these immortal words to the terrified occupant: 'Not very clever this morning, are we sir.'

I witnessed a similar incident in our quiet market town one Tuesday morning. Tuesday was Market Day, so all available parking spaces were reduced by half as the stall holders set up their trestles on the cobbles.

A very large Jaguar managed to get a parking space near to the bus stop, and the driver, an elderly lady of great dignity and breeding, complete with large floral hat, got out and locked the door with deliberation.

By the time she returned, the town was very busy, with traffic moving slowly in both directions vying for any available parking space.

I noted that my colleague was chatting amiably to one of the managers of the local supermarket, when I heard the unmistakeable sound of vehicular impact. Looking up, I saw the Jaguar had reversed straight out into the road, and collided with some force into a large Ford Cortina. I began to walk slowly towards the scene, when the elderly lady driver selected 'forward' and, with large hat tilting at a slightly drunken angle, shot forward in a screech of tyres and tortured metal. She then struck a small Mini parked alongside her original parking space. I hesitated. The large floral hat slid down her forehead, and I watched her reach under the dashboard area for another gear. Reverse. Whoosh, out she came again, ricocheting off her first target and, with spinning rear wheels, gunned straight across the road to hit three stationary cars parked on the opposite side. The bruised Jaguar rocked momentarily, then with a wheelspin worthy of Santa Pod, it accelerated past me in a long and wide turn under full steam. Pedestrians leapt for safety, as the Jaguar scattered some market stalls and struck the Gents toilet with an expensive 'crunch'. The floral hat had by now completely obscured the white and worried face, but the defiance to overcome this rampant steed was obvious as the frail figure lunged with her arm under the dash again.

'Watch out,' came the cry. 'She's coming back again.'

So she did. Torturous screams came from the sorely wounded wheel arches as the Jag howled rearwards again, its driver sightless but infinitely determined.

With a last sickening smash, the Jaguar finally came to rest embedded in between two family saloon cars innocently parked outside the meat emporium. The silence was deafening!

My colleague, who had watched the whole ghastly episode from the safety of a shop doorway, walked slowly across to the now quietly steaming Jaguar, and opened the door. He gently pushed the elderly lady's hat back on to her head, and helped her with elegant and escorting arm out of the remains.

'How opportune it was that you stopped, Lady Crudwell,' he stated, 'you left your eggs in the supermarket.'

16

Tough at the Sharp End

Once a month, the Police Federation send out a wonderful magazine to its members called simply *Police*. It has a wide range of articles written by very prominent men, news about upturns in the law and details of legislation which will invariably affect its members in the future. But the regular feature I always turn to first is a single page about two pages in from the front. Written by a highly intelligent and very funny man, it bears the title of his nom-de-plume, 'Dogberry'. Where he gets his information from in such detail is a mystery to me and thousands like me, but I have yet to meet a copper who doesn't automatically turn to this page before reading on into heavier matters. It is a page where egos come to die, where the bubble of autocratic pomposity falls on the sharpened quill and is popped in full public gaze. The stories make you laugh at the sheer audacity of some senior officers in the various forces, people who have made man-management a term of derision.

It was whilst reading such an article that I noted a name I had heard of some years previously. The senior officer, now very high up indeed in another force, had come into 'Dogberry's column with some outlandish statements regarding the car parking spaces reserved for ranks above Chief Inspector – a constant source of amusement. But I recalled a story about him as a

Detective Chief Inspector, as retold to me by a colleague who had been involved in the incident.

The DCI was newly promoted. Very newly promoted. In fact, he had been a uniformed inspector prior to this rapid elevation, but had been a detective constable many years before that. Quite a good dick at that, but times and promotion had made him change. As a uniformed inspector, he had been quite a pain in the lower regions to the men under his command, which took a lot of his old friends a bit by surprise. But then, they mused, some people do change with a rise in status, so sat back and let him get on with it.

With the new promotion, he seemed to get worse. His force was, like mine, a large rural one. Single officers maintaining the law over huge areas, and dealing with everything that came up. But the new DCI soon changed that. On paper, his idea was very good. In a town or city it would have been an undoubted bonus. All crime or suspected crime was to be reported to the local CID office, and no further investigation was to go forward until a DC had attended. It also applied to any sudden or unexpected deaths in the area. If a doctor couldn't sign a certificate, and the coroner was informed, then a DC would have to attend to ascertain whether crime could be ruled out.

In the rural areas, possibly thirty miles away from the nearest CID officer, this invariably began to cause delays. The local bobby would attend a sudden death, inform control, who would notify the CID, who would look around their office for someone who wasn't hidden behind a mountain of paperwork or up to their necks in an on-going investigation.

Relationships between the uniformed and plain clothes officers are usually very good, nothing like that portrayed by the popular crime series on TV. Both branches work together, invariably sharing their information. So it was doubly annoying for the CID to have to leave their investigations to travel out to an incident which had in the past been dealt with perfectly adequately by their uniformed colleagues. After all, the uniformed man on the spot was just as capable of detecting anything suspicious, and was probably more aware of the background to the death simply because he was the local bobby.

But the directive was unyielding.

So it was that one day, in a farmhouse many miles from civilization, a young farmhand was found dead in the toilet. The doctor attended, and notified the local bobby that he couldn't sign the death certificate. It was fairly obvious that the young man had fallen off the loo in a state of advanced drunkenness, cracked his head on the hand basin and died as a result.

It was arranged for the coffin to be brought to the scene, and CID informed as per orders. In the meantime, the local man made his enquiries from the grieving parents, took his statements, and did his best to comfort them.

When the carrier arrived with the coffin, there was still no sign of any CID man coming, and Constable D radioed the control to find out an ETA. None was forthcoming, but he was reminded that the body was to remain where it was until such time as a DC did turn up.

Constable D was not noted for his patience, and gave his opinion of both the order and the delay in no uncertain terms over the air. It was heard in its entirety by the DCI en route to his office. One can imagine his tight-lipped anger as he heard his newly-formed ideas being harangued over the air, aware that his standing, and that of his CID section, was being slated for all to hear. He informed the control that he would attend to this matter himself. He consoled himself with the thought that if the conversation between the damned 'wooden-top' and the control had been heard by officers of Command rank, it would merely emphasize his claims that his section was drastically under strength and that he was the right man for the job in that he could turn to and do it himself in a crisis.

Constable D was walking along the narrow concrete footpath outside the farmhouse with the farmer's wife, talking about her roses. His colleague, Constable Y, was standing looking out over the fields with the farmer, talking sheep and cross-breeding. None of them really wanted to sit in the house.

The new DCI arrived, and with a flourish of his hand signalled the two officers to follow him into the house to view the deceased. Once out of sight and earshot of the two civilians, he then began to berate the officers for their outspoken attitude to his orders. Both constables had worked with the DCI at various stages through his career, and it being far away from official earshot, and not recorded on tape, they let him know exactly what they thought of him, his daft ideas and how much extra pain it placed on the people involved.

Quite taken aback by their joint attack and its savagery, the DCI, knowing the two men to be quite unawed by his status, and neither of them bothered about promotion, decided to keep quiet. He merely confirmed the local man's diagnosis of the situation and told them curtly to 'get on with it'.

The two officers placed the deceased in the coffin, and with some difficulty began to negotiate its passage through the tight corners and narrow doorways of the farmhouse. The lad had been well built and was heavy, and the DCI could see his chance to impress the farmer and his wife with a display of organization, as the two officers struggled and sweated with the shell through the front door on to the path.

They paused for a while, to get their breath, and to give the old couple a chance to pay their respects. This

133

done, the two men, breathing hard, lifted the coffin up again. The DCI immediately took charge of the situation, and told them to put it back down. Organization! That was what was needed. The two constables were to take the heavy end, whilst he, despite his rank, would assist with the light end. So it was. The bobbies carried the head end, and the DCI, walking slowly backwards, carried the feet. The footpath was very narrow, and built up, such that there was a five-inch drop down to the rose borders on either side, and it was into this drop that the DCI suddenly slipped with his heel. A short yell burst from his lips, as laden with the coffin in both hands, he went over backwards to sit heavily down on the garden. Right on to a pruned rose bush. And I mean 'right on to it'.

The poor man was in agony, and very gingerly the two uniformed officers lifted him off his predicament. His ignominy was heightened when he was subjected to First Aid in the back of the carrier, bent forward and trousers around his ankles. The drive to the local hospital was discomfort personified, with the DCI standing in the back of the transit, wincing at every bump and turn of the road. He was rushed into casualty, and the two officers were informed that he would be kept in 'for observation'.

The humour of the whole incident struck them when they got outside, but they did feel a certain sympathy for the man. They would get him some sweets to help pass the hours. (It was fairly obvious that that was all he would pass in comfort for some time!) So, giggling like maniacs, they called into a sweet shop to see what would bring the DCI some pleasure.

'It would have to be something he likes,' mused Constable Y.

'Agreed,' stated Constable D. 'Something to remind him of the occasion.'

They both nodded earnestly. Chocolates, perhaps? Possibly some smooth toffees?

The DCI, lying face down in his hospital bed, was touched to see the two men return later that day, bearing wrapped packages which they placed on his bedside locker. A short chat about his welfare, then they left, to return to the scene and collect his car.

Their departure coincided with his nurse coming to take blood pressure and inspect the damaged area.

'Oh,' she said in surprise, 'how nice. You've got some sweets.'

'Help yourself,' said the DCI, his thoughts on lower matters.

'Oooh! How lovely,' the nurse cooed, peering into the plain wrapped packages, 'they're both my favourites. What a choice.'

'Really?' said the DCI, his curiosity aroused, 'what are they?'

'Oh, Roses and Thorntons.'

The DCI winced.

17

Pretty Vicious

WPC Sandeport stretched and shook her head violently. She glared balefully at her instructor who was grinning at her.

'C'mon girl, get up and get on with it.' She shook her numb arm and blinked to clear the sweat from her eyes. She tucked the top of her judogi into her green belt, and bowed.

'Why,' she wondered, 'have I volunteered for this course?' It looked interesting on the crew room notice board – Anyone interested in learning ju-jitsu. Contact PC W for details – and the extension number.

She had done self defence at the training school but it had never been like this! The first thing she had difficulty coming to grips with was the fitness. They did over an hour's fitness training in this class before they even started to practise the holds, kicks, punches, throws, nerve holds and all the other paraphernalia associated with the oldest of martial arts. She sighed, and made her move towards her still grinning instructor. Wallop!! Over she went again.

'Good! Very good. You're getting the idea of it. Now, do it to me.' He stood over her, tall and bearded, his bald head glistening with perspiration. She jumped up, and immediately felt a grip of iron clamp itself round her throat, cutting off her air supply and making her arch backwards. It was too tight, he never used force like this before! She struggled, trying to break the grip. No good. She groped for the thumb, to bend it back.

The cunning sod had tucked it in. Still the pressure did not decrease. She felt a feeling of something akin to panic sweeping her. No, not panic. Anger! She was getting damned cross! She swept her hips to one side, feeling his body follow the movement, then she switched in the other direction sharply, and drove back with her elbow into his stomach. A loud explosion of air went over her left shoulder as she felt her mark. Right! Now you're for it, she thought, as the arm grip lessened round her neck. She stamped down on his unprotected foot, and pulled the arm round her throat free as he went loose. Gripping the wrist in her left hand, she bent over forward and grabbed the underside of the right armpit of her instructor with her right hand, pulling him over her hip at the same time. It was so *easy*! Over he went in an excellent ippon seonage, to crash hard down on the canvas matting. Still gripping the arm at the wrist, she stepped over his back as he lay there, putting on an arm lever 'against the joint'. She then deliberately, and with a great amount of sadistic pleasure, kicked him hard in the ribs. Letting go, she stood back with arms folded, looking down at his twisted body. Slowly, he turned his head, and with the same infuriating grin on his face looked up at her.

'Feel better now?'

'Oh, *very* satisfactory!' she grinned down at him. What a lovely fella! She bowed, 'very satisfactory – Sensai,' she remembered to give him his title.

He jumped up on to his feet, patted her arm, then winced as she reacted by grabbing his fingers and bending them hard backwards until he dropped to his knees.

'Enough,' he grunted, 'get changed and showered and we'll all go for a cup of tea.'

She bobbed a bow at him, bowed at the door as she left and ran into the shower, feeling extremely happy.

Three months later, WPC Sandeport was driving the GP car around the small market town in the company of her friend, Joyce Blande. Due to lack of manpower, they were both on nights and in fact were the only uniformed officers on in the whole area for the shift.

The radio called them to go to the local taxi rank, where there was a call for assistance from a taxi driver, apparently having trouble with some off-duty soldiers.

When they attended, there was a lot of shouting and pushing and shoving, and they both got out of the car. Walking steadily over to the crowd, they were aware of a feeling of depression settling over the taxi driver, and an increase in the cocky attitude of the squaddies as they eyed the two attractive young women in the black slacks and tailored jackets coming towards them.

Ignoring the suggestive remarks made by the group of young soldiers, they spoke to the taxi driver.

'Where's your mates, then?' he asked nervously, hinting that perhaps they could do with some male officers.

'We don't need them for these,' Joyce laughed out loud, and nodded backwards with her head to the assembled squaddies in derisive fashion.

One of the young squaddies put an arm round her waist, and patted her backside in a condescending manner.

'Gi 'us a kiss, darlin'. Or perhaps you fancy something better?' He leered at his grinning mates. His grin changed to one of painful anguish as he felt his fingers bent backwards with a strength that made him rise up on his toes. He then went down on to the pavement as Joyce stepped towards his hand, and struck hard down and backwards with her clenched fist into his genitals. His mates stood aghast, as, puking into the gutter, he was informed that he was under arrest for breach of the peace.

One of his mates, striking a blow for dented masculinity, grabbed WPC Sandeport's wrist. He flinched as she feinted with her fingers at his eyes and, with his attention distracted, grabbed his wrist with two hands and twisted her full weight round. Caught unawares, he found his arm up his back in a hammer lock! A sharp kick behind the knees brought him down to the pavement, and he joined his colleague under arrest for breach of the peace. Two sets of handcuffs went on, and they were escorted to the car, where they sheepishly got in without fuss. WPC Sandeport stood by the car as Joyce went back to the stunned group.

'Do we have to lock you all up?' she demanded, hands on hips.

They climbed into the taxi without a quarrel.

'Thanks love,' the taxi driver smiled at her.

'S'right,' she stated, and turned on her heel back to the car.

Now, this anecdote is not in itself particularly funny unless you happen to be a woman reading this chapter, or are a policewoman who is fed up with being on permanent office duty because of your sex, or you happen to be in the office when two very dejected squaddies are brought in by two policewomen who are two thirds their prisoners' size!

My wife pointed out that the 'girls' had been given no mention in this book other than the odd brief sentence where they got a rough deal. So, I hope this brings the great work the WPCs do in this job to the attention of the reader. These two girls I actually taught, and it wasn't until a few years afterwards that I heard how their learning had been put into practice with such confidence and ability. Next time you fancy your chances against the members of the police who wear skirts, remember – they could be the two mentioned above!

18

Fluffy Tales

Dealing with people is one of the bonuses of this job. Whilst they make you cry, make you wonder at the sanity of humanity, or make you feel disgust at the way one human can treat another, they also give you laughter, happiness, and a feeling of well-being by their acts of kindness. They can also cause acute embarrassment!

Women cause me the most embarrassment due, I suppose, to the fact that when they want their husbands they are never around! Especially in times of crisis. So they look for the first available man they can trust and most people trust the policeman.

The times I have seen recorded incidents which have involved women who have locked themselves out of their cars, their houses, locked their children in the house or their dog in the car. They've been stuck in baths, they've been stuck up ladders and one memorable young woman was stuck in the washing machine! The trouble is, that in a lot of cases, the apparel these women are wearing, or *not* wearing, is the most embarrassing! For instance, take the young lady a colleague dealt with, the one who had stuck herself in the washing machine.

A woman approached him in the street and, as is usually the case, asked him if he was married! It is a constant source of amusement to me that women assume a man is 'safe' merely because he is married. Something to do with matrimonial neutering, I suppose. Anyway, on hearing that he was, she then divulged the information that a friend of hers was in a predicament that required delicacy, and so saying, took him to a well-kept semi-detached house further down the road.

There, to his amazement, he was confronted by the shapely outline of a young woman's bottom staring him in the face from out of a twin tub! A naked bottom, even!

Apparently what had happened, he was told in a resonant voice which came from deep within the bowels of the washing machine, she had been washing, and decided to bung her night attire into the machine to make up the load. She undressed in the kitchen, having pulled the curtains, and popped the clothing into the tub. She made herself a cup of tea whilst she stood waiting, still naked, as she had decided to unload the wash tub into the spinner tub, then go for a bath. At the end of the wash cycle, she unloaded everything into the spinner tub, but had noticed something gleaming down in the bottom of the washer. Apparently it was a small brooch of great sentimental value belonging to her young daughter, which had come off a tee shirt when being washed. She leaned into the washer, only to find that the brooch had slipped down through the hole behind the impeller blade. She had probed further, and then discovered, to her horror, that her fingers were stuck fast in the gap. She had struggled to free herself, but found that the fastened fingers had swollen up. So there she was; naked, upside down, and head and shoulders in the wash tub!

My colleague, being a man of some resourcefulness, realized that first he had to attend to the lady's dignity, and with the neighbour, found a sheet to cover her obvious charms. Then, after much hysterical hilarity, they had managed to move the washing machine into the centre of the kitchen where he could get to the back of the machine. Once this was done, it was a simple matter to release the unfortunate woman's trapped fingers with the use of cold water and liquid soap. It was a very red-faced but grateful young woman who emerged from the tub, to be confronted by a grinning young officer.

'All in a day's work, madam,' he had said, with a diplomacy which should have made him first in line for Foreign Secretary. She, on the other hand, thinking only of the object of her downfall, had asked him if the brooch was there to be retrieved, and as he peered back into the depths of her erstwhile prison, asked innocently, 'Can you see anything?'

'I think, madam,' he said with downcast eyes, 'that I have seen everything there is to see.' And pulling the sheet about her, she fled upstairs!

I had a similarly embarrassing experience one night when I was making my way to our sub-divisional headquarters for petrol. It was a cold and blustery night, and nothing appeared to be moving on the roads at all. As I approached the outskirts of the town, I caught a glimpse of something pale, flitting up the footpath of the main road. I stopped, and got out, as I was sure the headlights had picked out something not quite right. How very true! As I walked over the large grass verge which bordered the main road, I saw the distinct outline of a female figure, very lightly clad, running up the road towards me.

Dressed only in a pink negligee, and in her early thirties, the young woman rushed up to me, her negligee streaming in the wind behind her, and literally threw herself at me. She wrapped her arms around my neck in a grip of iron, and her legs went around my legs in an equally fervent grip! In a voice which reeked with whisky, she implored me not to let 'him' get her. At this point, a gentleman, dressed in loud Paisley patterned pyjamas and silk dressing robe came thundering around the corner. I was struggling to release myself from the lady's arms and legs with as much dignity as I could muster.

'I'm terribly sorry, officer,' he stated in booming tones, 'she's had too much to drink I fear. Deidre,' this to the woman still attached limpet-like to my uniform, 'Deidre, release this officer at once!'

He came round behind me, so he was looking at his wife's face, and there then ensued a verbal exchange over my shoulder as accusation and counter-accusation flew in a domestic battle! I, in the meantime, was standing bemusedly on the footpath with this damned woman still wrapped round my body! What was worse, her negligee was very flimsy, and rising in great fluttering waves high in the air as the wind blustered about us.

At this point, of course, the up to then empty roads suddenly filled with the traffic which had been missing! Headlights from every angle, which could not fail to see the stationary police car, and the near naked woman wrapped around a policeman, being berated by what must have appeared to be a cuckolded husband! I tried to move, but the grips tightened. I mean, how do you walk with dignity towards your car with a nude woman wrapped around your legs? So I shuffled backwards into the driveway of a house, and took refuge with my shrieking limpet behind a large beech hedge. Her husband followed, still booming about her excessive drinking habits, and that she was only making the matter worse by insisting on keeping 'this constable' from his normal duties!

Finally, in a supreme effort of strength, I managed to detach the lady from my person, and covered her with my greatcoat. Together, we all walked back to her house, where she then dissolved into tears and, grabbing hold of me, implored me not to tell the papers! I merely nodded dumbly, and beat a hasty retreat back to my car.

I recounted this story to the night crew who were in

143

the office as I arrived in a state of advanced shock, hoping they would believe me. They did! To my delight, the office man stated that this was an occurrence which came to pass about once a month, with such regularity in fact, that the more unscrupulous members of the shifts deliberately walked around that area in the hope they might be the one who was grabbed!!

Policemen also have moments of self-inflicted embarrassment, usually of a very minor form – a typical example of which is when you are bursting for a pee, but have had no chance to get one. Bladder the size of a football, you finally manage to find a dark pull-in or layby, and make a hasty dive for the nearest bushes. Just as you're experiencing what should be the crowning moment of the shift, a car will draw up and the driver will get out, talking to his or her passenger, saying, 'Well he *must* be around here somewhere,' in a tone that makes it quite obvious he or she wishes to talk to a policeman. You are then left with the task of stopping 'midstream' and then nonchalantly making your appearance in a manner that shows you have been inspecting the back of the hedge in the interests of crime prevention. No matter how brusque or off-hand you are, *you* know *they* know exactly what you were doing!

Another embarrassing moment I heard of occurred some years ago in the Midlands area, and involved a squash club which reported that members' valuables and articles of clothing were going missing from the changing rooms. A special effort was made in regard to this complaint, the Superintendent being the Chairman of the club. So a hidden camera was installed in the male members' changing rooms. After a week the film was processed and the members of the CID and uniformed team sat down to catch their criminal.

Imagine their surprise when all that was shown was a rather sordid little piece of action featuring a businessman and the wife of a local councillor, and the naked form of one of the police members of the club wandering about in bemusement looking for his clothes which had been stolen!!

Another young officer suffered untold indignities when he attended a report of a lady who had locked herself out of her car. He duly turned up at the car park situated at the local beauty spot near the river, and with a smugness that only youth can provide, walked in a slow and business-like manner over to the lady and her car, a cynical half smile of condescension on his face. His chauvanistic approach and his attitude of such supreme masculine ego must have annoyed the lady to the point of screaming! But she obviously bit her tongue and was suitably fluttery and feminine as the door of her car was almost casually flipped open by means of a knife, screwdriver and tape.

Smiling benevolently to all who had witnessed his supremacy over the female sex's inability to even carry a spare key, he reached for the doorhandle of his car. To his horror, it wouldn't open, and he saw the keys dangling from the ignition in open mockery of his mistake! What was worse, he had left his radio on the passenger seat!

Aware that the eyes of the world were upon him, he grinned weakly, and decided that he could still maintain his air of complete control if he went for a stroll along the car park to a telephone situated at the river's edge. This he did, maintaining his attitude of self-confident bonhomie. He even paused to chat to a young lad fishing over the river wall, talking loudly in knowledgable tones about chub and perch. Leaning over to look at what type of float the lad was using, he felt his helmet slip and, grabbing desperately, watched in misery as it hit the raging torrent, and disappeared over the thundering waterfall out of sight.

At this point, an elderly lady came up to him, having witnessed his anguish, and commiserated, especially when, she told him, he could have used the telephone for someone to fetch him another one, but wasn't it a pity that the phone had been vandalized!!

19

No Shades of Grey

In every police force there is a 'character'. A man who becomes famous throughout the force, and the stories about him go on long after he retires, becoming more and more humorous and outlandish with every telling. Most of the stories are from a time when the law meant something, and the stringent paperwork which dominates the modern force was only a fraction of what it is today. In fact, woe betide the policeman who wandered in during his shift to sit in the office at a typewriter. Out on the streets was where policemen belonged, and spending so much time with the public, their reputations grew.

The next two anecdotes concern a very dear man, retired now, although he stuck it out well into his early sixties before going, and who I count as a great friend. He is also someone I miss dreadfully when the going gets rough, or the bosses are on my back. I shall call him Harris, but should he ever read this book he will see himself and recall those evenings spent on the streets with me by his side, regaling me with his tales of yesteryear. Bless you, Harris. I miss your comradeship to this day.

The first story is set in the early sixties, but first let me introduce Harris to you. A stocky man, going bald, with thinning hair grey over his head. Clean shaven, and shoes polished, he still managed to look remarkably like a car park attendant in his flat hat. Thin-rimmed glasses and pointed features, he had a ready laugh, especially when telling jokes or stories about himself, a full-blooded belief in the law and everything it stood for. There were no shades of grey, he was a man of such apparent honesty that his comments caused him a great deal of heart-ache and trouble with his conscience. A man who trod where angels fear to tread, and trod hard, and a brusque manner with senior officers that brought him more postings in his career than anyone else in the force! Such was Harris.

On this particular day, he had been told to drive the GP car. Why, even he doesn't know, but it had something to do with force policy that everyone should be able to do the other bloke's job, or at least have an insight into its workings. So they gave him an enormous Ford Zephyr saloon, complete with two-tone horn and a blue light.

Off went Harris, ecstatic that this recent posting had found him behind the wheel of such a wonderful car. He took it on to the only stretch of road worth driving on to do the car justice. Now, as I say, we are talking about the fifties and early sixties, when dual carriageways and motorways were in their infancy and restricted to the south of England. The only stretch of road worthy of the Zephyr was thirty odd miles of three-lane 'A' road. You know the sort, one north, one south and one in the middle for crashes.

Harris was enjoying the moment. Using the centre lane, he watched the traffic part before him as drivers saw the police car approach in their mirrors.

Suddenly, the traffic didn't part. On the contrary, it came to a halt. In front of him, Harris could see an enormous traffic jam. Switching on headlights, blue light and two-tone horn, Harris turned on to the verge and drove down the steaming lines of traffic, aware that the eyes of hundreds were upon him and the uniform in which he was staunchly proud.

Finally, he could go no further. There in front of him was the hunt. Horses, hounds, hunting pink, horns braying and whips cracking as they quartered back and forth across the main road. Harris selected the public address system fitted to the Zephyr.

'This is the police,' he bellowed above the din, his words echoing around the men and women of the hunt. 'I repeat, this is the police. Clear the road immediately. You are causing an obstruction of the highway. I say again, clear the road this instant.'

It had some effect, as the huntsman rode up to the car and leaned down to speak into the open window.

'Charley's in there somewhere,' he gesticulated with his crop at the thicket and long grass at the side of the way. 'Got to flush him out so we can continue the sport, don't cha-know.' He grinned in what Harris thought a typically superior and conservative fashion, and as the only practising socialist in the force, which had got him more than one posting, Harris took umbrage at both the attitude and the manner in which the words were delivered.

'I don't care if Fred, Archie or Harold is in there, get this road cleared,' he roared.

Another horse trotted up, with a large man wearing a florid complexion as dark as his hunting pink.

'Won't be a minute, my man,' he said to Harris, a term which was guaranteed to make the officer's hackles rise. 'Soon be orff once Charley's flushed out.'

'Who are you?' Harris's voice boomed out over the PA.

'I'm the Master,' came the reply.

'Does that mean you're in charge?' Harris asked out of the window, but his question transmitted to the by now highly impressed motoring public, who could see their taxes being well spent in this little confrontation.

'Well, yes. Yes it does.' The florid man was beginning to get a little flustered.

'Then I'm telling you that if these animals are not moved in ten seconds, I shall arrest you for obstruction of the highway.'

The waiting motorists began to silently mouth a countdown from ten.

'Now look here . . .,' the Master started, and banged his riding crop down on the roof of the Zephyr to emphasize a point, 'this really is too . . .'

He got no further. Harris was out of the Zephyr, and minutely inspecting the clean white roof of the patrol car. A diminutive mark showed in the painted surface, and that was enough.

'Right!' Harris wheeled to face the florid Master, 'you are under arrest for wilful obstruction of the highway, and causing malicious damage to a police car.'

With that, the florid man was dragged, with some pulling and tugging, from his steed, to be handcuffed and shoved unceremoniously into the back of the patrol car. Harris regained his driving seat, and lifted the handset again.

'I have arrested one of your number for obstruction. Now, the rest of you get off the road or I shall get out and do the same to you.'

Just how he was going to get the whole hunt into the back seat of the Zephyr God only knows, but it worked. The mass of horses and riders, dogs and followers moved hurriedly off the main road and on to the verges. Harris then climbed out of his car, and brought the traffic on with huge armfuls of air.

He drove the Ford back the way he had travelled, pausing only to stop after a few miles to question his prisoner.

'What is your name?' he enquired.

'Bagdale,' came the reply.

'I didn't ask you where you came from. I asked you your name.'

'And I told you, it's Bagdale.'

150

'Nothing else?' Harris enquired.

'That's all you have to know,' the florid man countered.

'Right,' said Harris. 'Failing to give your name and address to a police constable in uniform. That's another charge you've got saddled with – if you'll pardon the pun.' He put his pocket book away, and started back up the road.

Arriving at the police station a bit later on, he parked the Zephyr and dragged his prisoner out of the back seat. A firm grip on the man's collar helped propel him down the corridor towards the Charge Office. From his office doorway, the Chief Inspector saw a flash of pink whip past his line of vision, and shouted after Harris's back.

'What have you brought in this time, Harris?'

'Obstruction of the highway, failing to give name and address, and I firmly believe he is a candidate for the funny farm. Kept telling me where he lived. Just said Bagdale a few times. Must have fallen off his horse.'

The Chief Inspector nodded from behind his desk, adjusted his spectacles and bent to his reports. Suddenly he stopped, frozen in mid bend.

Obstruction? Pink coat? Horses? BAGDALE!!! – Dear God!

He leaped from his chair with sufficient force to send it skittering backwards, and dashed into the corridor in time to hear the cell doors close with a resounding clang. Harris, fed up with his prisoner already, and tired of waiting for the duty sergeant, had 'banged him up'.

The Chief Inspector raced down the corridor, heart pounding as he sensed the coveted crown of Superintendent fly gracefully out of the window. Pushing Harris aside in his panic, he unlocked the great metal door to the cell, and swung it open.

Harris watched as the Chief Inspector's right knee

took on a slight, but noticeable, deferential dip and the hand strayed up towards a non-existent forelock.

'Oh, your Grace, your Grace. I must apologize. There has been a terrible mistake. Oh my God . . .' Harris noted the hands twisting round in Uriah Heep fashion as the Chief bowed and curtsied his way into the austere surroundings of cell one.

'Aagh!', The cry was wrung from the senior officer as he spotted the handcuffs still around the mottled wrists of the prisoner.

'HARRIS!' He swung round to face the impassive constable. 'Do you know who this is? Have you any idea what you have done? Don't you know the aristocracy always give their surname only?' He was almost in tears. A haunted look at the Duke of Bagdale sitting on a hard cell bed, then, 'And handcuffs! Are you mad, man?' He seemed lost for words.

Harris sighed and, taking his handcuffs key from his pocket, released the prisoner.

The Chief brushed him away, and forced down a desire to massage the reddened wrists. The Duke of Bagdale! Friend of the Chief Constable. Chairman of the Watch Committee.

'Oh your Grace, your Grace,' the Uriah Heep act came on again. 'How can I apologize?'

'Harris!' he turned back to the constable. 'You're posted. Get out. I never want to see your face here again. Posted! Do you hear? Effective as from now! Get your things and GO!'

He ushered the florid Duke of the Realm towards his office and the bottle of whisky hidden behind the volume relating to the licensing law.

Harris sighed, and began to collect his things from his locker. They'd been in there almost three days . . .

Harris stood sheltering from the icy blast that whipped up off the North Sea to dash itself against his yielding body. His thick cape lifted and swelled around him, and he put a tentative hand out to pull at the peak of his cap which, despite the restraining chin strap, threatened to fly off his head at any moment.

Nothing is worse in this world than a seaside resort out of season, unless it's a seaside resort out of season and in the depths of one of the most savage winters ever recorded. Harris squinted against the driving snow, and stamped his feet on the packed snow underfoot, which did nothing to eliminate the cold, and only made the surface below his chilled toes even more slippery. He cocked his ear against the wind's moan, peering out of his doorway at the telephone box across the road. Faintly he heard its bell jangle and, sighing deeply, he followed like Pavlov's dogs towards its call. He had been standing in that awful shop doorway for ten minutes, well before his point time, and had kept out of sight in case the duty sergeant came along to give him a 'chalk' personally.

Huddling in the warm sanctuary of the kiosk, Harris lifted the receiver.

'Harris?' the voice of Sergeant Wellbeloved boomed through the handset.

'Yes, Sar'nt.' Harris wondered who else it could have been, out in this awful bloody snow and wind. There was only Archie Allinson on this side, and he was on the other side of his beat.

'Ah, Harris,' Wellbeloved seemed satisfied that he had the right man. 'I shall see you at your next point, that's E3 on your card, and also Allinson. I do not expect to see you standing idly together, chattering or smoking. It's bad for the image. Half an hour, then.' The phone went dead with a 'click', leaving Harris looking bemusedly into the now buzzing instrument. He sighed.

Who would be out at half past midnight, in a howling gale, at an empty church on the top of the cliffs, standing in a churchyard which looked like the setting for a Dracula film, just to complain that two bobbies who

153

were there had been chatting? He replaced the receiver, and looking wistfully round the warm, almost stuffy interior of the callbox, thrust open the door and went out into the raging elements.

Trudging slowly, his feet slipping and sliding on the snow-covered pavement, Harris rattled doorhandles all the way up through the town's old quarters until he came to the foot of the one hundred and ninety-nine steps which led ever upwards from sanity towards the maelstrom which he knew would greet him at the top. Hauling himself up by use of the metal handrail set into the stone wall, Harris slithered and cursed his way to the top of the steps. Looking back, he noted that the stairs disappeared from view within six feet of him, hidden by the horizontal driving snow. He spat out errant flakes and, head down, dragged himself up the last remaining steps to the top. Well, not quite the top. The footpath leading from the top step sloped upwards out of sight, its paving-stone surface hidden under eighteen inches of snow.

Leaning at an impossible angle against the wind, Harris staggered towards the dark shape that showed fleetingly in between the squalls of snow. Sanctuary indeed! Gasping, he entered the dark recess, the warmth of the place emphasized by the wind's raging a few feet away.

Seated on the benches thoughtfully provided by the parish for its church, set into the foyer walls, his feet up and his face lit by the warm glow of a cigarette, sat Constable Archie Allinson.

'Now then, Mr Harris,' his voice sounded smug and self satisfied,' Old Wellbeloved got you as well then?' Harris nodded, too breathless to answer. Allinson went on with a grin in his voice.

'Wellbeloved. What a name for the most anti-social bastard ever to don a copper's uniform, eh? Pity he took an instant dislike to you. I suppose it's because he sees you as a troublemaker, having had so many postings in one year. Never mind, he'll be ages yet. Can't reach us by phone, and the old Popular will never make it up Green Lane in this snow. We'll give him twenty minutes or so, then nip back the quick way and get to the station in time for our meal break. If he does make it up here, he'll probably take us back in the car, seeing as how he'll need the ballast. Take the weight off your feet,' he slid his wet boots off the bench and loosened his heavy cape. Harris sat down gratefully and took his cap off, loosening the tight high-necked collar on his cape as well.

Outside the weather battered the town and cliffs, and Harris pondered on the sanity of the powers that be in sending policemen out on such a night. Any criminal worth his salt was tucked up in a warm bed, not out in this atrocious blizzard blagging gaffs all over town. He sighed again, and silently shook his head.

He felt his head nodding, and jerked himself awake. Old Wellbeloved would go mad if he found his officers asleep on the job. That was even worse than idly chattering.

'That's it, then. Five minutes after point time,' Archie Allinson replaced the huge silver Hunter back into his top pocket and stood up. Harris looked up at him and shook his head.

'I'm not moving yet. I've got to go all the way down to Green Lane, then along the bottom road. I'll be shagged before I get half way . . .', he paused as Archie held up a restraining hand.

'I told you I'd show you the quick way down. We can't go down the steps, Old Wellbeloved will be parked down there waiting to pounce on us. I know him of old. No, we go out of the churchyard, along the footpath, then cut down through the snicket and follow the hill to the bottom. It brings us out at the back of the fishermen's cottages. Then you go left for a hundred yards, and down the steps to the road. If he's waiting, well, you've been checking the backs of property. I go right, and follow the backs into the old quarter, bringing me out by the old tower. If he's there, then I've been checking property. He won't believe us, but he can't prove anything. C'mon.' His broad back disappeared out of the arched entrance into the snow. Harris fastened his collar, and wrapped his cape firmly around his body.

Side by side, they teetered their way through the churchyard, the snow now ever deepening. Archie seemed to know intimately every leaning headstone as he made for the churchyard gate.

Once on the road, the wind blew from behind them, and they made very fast progress to the place which Archie kept shouting was the 'quick way'. Only it was gone. Not only hidden by three feet of snow, but all landmarks below obliterated from view to indicate its approximate position. It was also apparently covered by a building site, judging by the bricks and rubbish piled about in the gloom. Archie's torch flashed and flitted from side to side.

'F . . . it!' He scanned the surrounding snow-covered hillocks and hummocks for a clue. Nothing.

He probed deeper into the now unknown territory, then swore again as his shin came up against something sharp. He kicked at the offending cause of his injury, and the rounded end of a corrugated iron sheet reared up out of the snow-laden workings. He looked back at Harris, a wild grin on his face, then beckoned him over. Leaning into the wind, he yelled into Harris's ear.

'The kids have been using this as a sledge! We'll do the same. C'mon. We'll be down the bottom in no time.' He pulled and tugged at the sheet until it was totally exposed. Kneeling on it to keep it down on the ground, he indicated that Harris should sit on. Harris grinned, and jumped on to the front, jamming his feet under the

ection which had been bent backwards. Archie shoved
ard, aiming more through sense of direction than by
xactitude, and as the sheet picked up speed, hopped
imbly on behind Harris.

'Should be down the bottom in no time!' he yelled
bove the wind. But no. The sheet tottered to a halt,
ilted forward downhill, but no movement.

'Too heavy!' yelled Archie, then, 'Undo our capes.
hey'll act as sails,' Harris nodded, and undid the
uttons down his cape, leaving only the collar slip and
hain acting as a fastening. Gripping the edges, he
pread his arms and, looking over his shoulder, saw
llinson doing the same. That did it!

The acceleration was phenomenal! Feet braced, and
aughing like maniacs, they whooped downwards.

There was no form of steerage, and neither of them
ould see anything ahead, so both were totally unready
or the terrific impact they encountered as they collided
ith the recently dug road built into the hillside.
lready disorientated by the snow, the two officers spun
ildly about on their sledge as it careered over the
acked surface then, with a stomach-heaving dip, con-
nued downwards at an ever faster pace. Harris, des-
erately gripping at the sides of the bucking sheet, was
ware that Archie was gone. Either by mistake or in the
terests of self preservation, he had deserted the rap-
lly sinking ship.

Harris was aware of a light shining faintly through the
loom, before it was blotted out by the swirling snow.
ear God, the cottages! In front and below! He threw
imself desperately off his charger to hit the snow with
bone-shaking thud. Rolling down to a stop, covered in
now, which had also packed itself tightly up his trouser
gs, he was aware of a muted, but very distinctive crash
f glass. The corrugated sheet, free of its weight, had
fted up in the wind and literally taken off to fly with
nerring accuracy through a large plate window of one

157

of the cottages. All this Harris saw as he stumbled down to the sloping back gardens of the houses. The light had gone, but in the reflected glare of the solitary light situated at the end of the path which surrounded the cottages, Harris could see about three feet of sombre black rippled metal poking out of the shattered window. He ran down the path, and on to the road in front of the houses, then doubled back to the house which had taken the full attack. To his horror, he saw the black Ford Popular supervision car parked outside the front door. Bloody hell, Wellbeloved had got there first!

Banging on the door, he was relieved to see a middle-aged woman, white with shock, standing in the hall. She was trembling violently, and clutching a very thin and very revealing negligee around her obvious and ample curves.

'Are you alright?' Harris asked nervously. The woman nodded, then stammered: 'He's upstairs. You'd better go up.' She stood to one side as Harris dashed past and bounded up the narrow stairway two at a time.

He entered the bedroom facing the hillside, and switched on his torch. The wind howled through the smashed window, making the curtains stand out horizontally from the wall. The offending sheet of metal flapped and clanked against the top of the dressing table, so Harris shoved it back out the window. Not a shrewd move, as it happened, because the wind casually flipped it up and out of sight over the rooftops! Harris groaned. Then he heard another groan, and turning round saw the figure of Sergeant Wellbeloved getting up from the floor by the bed, rubbing the back of his head. Harris also noted that the fat sergeant's legs were *not* dressed in regulation serge trousers, nor was his ample frame sporting his uniform jacket. On the contrary, he was clad merely in his shirt, and the collar had been removed from that!

Harris was aware of Archie Allinson entering the bedroom, his torch flicking from the window to the bed, from the bed to the half-dressed and groaning sergeant, and then on to Harris's face.

'Outside, Harris. Quick!' He clattered downstairs with Harris in his wake.

Outside, the Popular stood, its windscreen totally smashed by a large sheet of corrugated iron sheeting. Harris thought he was going to vomit. He looked at Archie, then they both began to laugh. Poor old Wellbeloved. Forever under their thumbs! He would know that only they could get him out of this fix, once he came round.

Sitting in the warm front parlour of Wellbeloved's police house, Harris helped himself to another glass of the amber liquid that the sergeant, now heavily bandaged about the head, tipped towards him in the rapidly emptying decanter. Archie Allinson slid an unregulation green sock from his boot, and scratched the back of his calf with an errant toe that peeked through the wool.

Wellbeloved grinned weakly at them, and they grinned back. Wellbeloved's missus came in, her thin, pinched features taking in the two officers drinking in her parlour. She sniffed, and thumped a plate of sandwiches down on the table before flouncing out again. Wellbeloved grinned even more weakly.

'She doesn't like drink,' he began, 'Methodist, y'see . . .' his voice trailed miserably off.

'You can rely on us, Sarge,' Archie grinned conspiratorially at him, 'after all, it was hardly your fault that your car was hit by a sheet of corrugated iron, was it? It's a good job that Harris and I were in the area to witness the whole thing. Strange that, two pieces of sheeting taking off as they did. One hitting the Widow Stark's window and the other hitting your car. Saw it all we did. Must get on to the foreman of that site first

159

thing in the morning, make him fasten his gear away
He looked across at Harris, who nodded sagely in reply

They stood up, and Wellbeloved looked at them with
eyes like a spaniel.

'You won't say anything. Promise?'

'Not a word, Sarge.'

'After all, Sarge,' Harris stated, 'you've got trouble
enough. Especially when your missus puts two and two
together and realizes that the sheet of metal came
through the front windscreen and hit you on the *back* of
the head!'

They let themselves out, and wandered down to the
station, feeling that despite the weather, things were
going to get a lot brighter in the days to come.

So, Harris, my old friend, I hope that this chapter
does you credit. I hope that you will look on it as my
contribution to your legend. I know that you have
hundreds of anecdotes like that, but those are two which
made me laugh until I cried. Few people, especially
those in authority, had any inkling of the tremendously
impish humour which pervaded your stern façade. I
wish there were more like you around today, it would
have been a lot more fun!

20

Scales of Justice

Anyone who has ever had to appear in a court of law will
now what an ordeal it can be. So spare a thought for
he policeman, who has to attend on a fairly regular
asis.

The function of the court is to hear both sides of the
rgument, eloquently put forward by learned members
f the legal profession and presided over by either a
udge or a bench of magistrates.

The former is a man chosen by his peers in the legal
rofession. His decision is, in the main, final and in
ome cases, he can direct a jury to come to a decision.
The latter are ordinary men and women who, usually
hrough position or standing in the community, are
hosen to represent justice in cases which are less
erious. They sit in a threesome on the bench and are
uided throughout by the Clerk of the Magistrates,
usually a local solicitor.

My own opinion of the courts is that the whole
rocedure is like a game of chess, with the battle
winging from one side to the other as it progresses.
ndeed, I once remonstrated with a Defence Counsel
fter a harrowing cross-examination in the Crown Court,
where my integrity and honesty were brought into
question and, in my opinion, great disrepute. He
emoved his wig, and looked up at me, 'It's all a game,
Constable. That's all. A game. Where the best man
wins, where the actor with the best lines can swing the

jury his way; right or wrong, it's a fact. I was losing. You were uncertain and unprepared for my questions. You faltered, I struck, and the case was mine. Don't take it to heart, old chap, I know your honesty is beyond reproach. His Honour knows it, and so does the jury. But I look for a chink in every inch of armour, and yours showed. So I stab. You lose your undoubted presence for a second, you stumble in your reply, and the jury senses the killer blow. They are watching for my upraised sword and give the thumbs down. It is a play on words, on a raised eyebrow in the jury's direction at exactly the right moment. It is also my playground, and you are a visitor, so you play to my rules. A game, old chap,' he patted my arm in a fatherly manner, and began to walk away.

'But what about justice?' I called after him.

'Justice? Justice? That *is* justice, officer. That is what it's all about. I believe my client to be innocent of the charge laid. I fight for that principle. If you or your prosecution people cannot lay the case such that I offer "no evidence", or I advise my client to plead guilty with mitigation, then that is your fault. My job is to work for my client to my best ability. If that means I have to sully your good name, or bring an element of doubt into the case against your procedure or attitude, then so be it. He was beginning to get a little rattled.

'But the bastard was guilty! He's got previous as long as your arm, and I caught him bang to rights on the premises. Dammit, he even coughed it! Where's the justice in letting him go free to do it again?'

He stepped close up to me.

'Officer. You may think he's guilty. I may think he's guilty. But on the evidence you produced and the manner in which it was put forward, the court didn't think he was. That is justice. If you make an allegation, then prove it. Without any element of doubt. You couldn't. So chalk it down to experience. Don't take it o heart.' Again the pat on the arm and he was gone, eaving me seething.

But on reflection, I know that he was right. So, plod n.

On the other hand, I have had some lovely battles in he magistrates' courts with solicitors, men I have a drink with or socialize with when not locked in battle. Especially in my local court, where I am known to the bench.

I recall one case with great relish. It had come about when I was on a police driving course, a periodical break from routine policing where every officer has to undergo a month's driving under tuition to refresh his good driving habits and eliminate his bad ones.

It was at a time when there was a petrol shortage, and a temporary but statutory speed limit of fifty miles an hour was imposed on all major roads.

We were on the A1 heading north and approaching a series of roadworks. Myself, two colleagues and a civilian instructor were all packed into a Ford Cortina. It was an innocuous plain blue, with a small badge on the rear bumper stating that it was a police vehicle and the driver was undergoing instruction.

I was behind the wheel, and on checking my mirror at the approach to the roadworks, saw a large Rover coming up behind at a high rate of knots. The driver began to flash his headlights at me, and drove so close to the rear of my vehicle that I expected him to shunt us. I could see his mouth working furiously as he flashed and cursed, then suddenly, he was gone. In a scattering of traffic cones and yellow plastic road lamps, he was alongside us, swearing and gesticulating with a single upraised finger at me through his side window. (Apparently I didn't even warrant two fingers, in his opinion!) He then proceeded to accelerate away up the area coned off for the pending roadworks, and in another skittering of red and white plastic, interspersed with yellow lamps, cut in front of a heavily laden wagon back on to the open road again.

Once past the roadworks, we gave chase. But as the average height of the three of us was about six feet, and our individual weights balanced out at about twelve stone, the Cortina with its sixteen hundred engine was sorely pressed to drag us up to eighty miles an hour. The Rover was well away at a speed far in excess of that. But we clung on to him, following his progress as he weaved and dodged in and out of the traffic, which was forced to jink and swerve as he cut and thrust his way through it.

But as fast as a Rover can go in the hands of a maniac, it cannot beat the speed of a radio wave! A traffic car was waiting for him at Scotch Corner, and that was where we found him some time later. A dapper young man, immaculately dressed in a grey suit, leaning nonchalantly on his bonnet and casually smoking a small cigar. We got out of the wheezing Cortina, and went across to speak with him. On seeing me, he stood up off the bonnet, and walked across to me.

'I am making an official complaint about your driving,' he stated, poking me in the chest with a well manicured finger.

Against *me*? I was gobstruck!

'You deliberately obstructed me back there, and shall be making allegations to that effect to your superiors.' Again the finger jabbed against my chest.

I fought down the urge to slap his wrist, and removed my pocket book. Then, as calmly as I could, asked, 'Your name and address, sir, and the name and address of the keeper of this vehicle. I also require to see your driving documents, and also a current certificate of insurance.'

'I am already late for an appointment, thanks to you, and I am writing to my MP to complain about this unlawful stopping and my harassment. I am now going to continue my journey, and any details you want I shall give to my local station when I get home. In the meantime, Constable, I want your number.' Again the finger poked at me. That did it! The wagging arm was gripped, and a Home Office approved arm lock went on. Then I advised him that he was under arrest for driving in a reckless, dangerous and careless fashion within my view, and for subsequently refusing to give his name and address on demand to a police officer in uniform. His bluster went down like a deflated balloon, and a weak grin came over his face, but to no avail. Into the traffic car he went!

Much later during the year, I was warned of a 'not guilty' court appearance, and turned up at our local courthouse. I had made a file up myself, and it had been checked and double-checked by my bosses. Reckless Driving – and he deserved it. The Cortina had been checked regarding the speedometer calibration, and found to be accurate. Statements had been taken by officers from my colleagues, the lorry driver at the roadworks, and three irate motorists who had stopped at the scene to complain about the man's manner of driving.

Into court we went.

The driver was represented by a barrister, not a solicitor. Complete in wig and gown, which I assume he thought would look impressive to the little 'hick' bench he was to face. His brief was tied in red tape, and his manner was one of great superiority.

The court rose, and in came the bench. I knew them all. There was Mrs Dibjohn from the electrical shop, Mr Viney from the papershop and Mr Barraclough, a local headmaster, sitting as chairman. The QC began to puff.

I left the court, to sit and wait in the witnesses' room, along with the three irate motorists, my three colleagues, the civilian instructor and the lorry driver. Our local Inspector was prosecuting.

One by one, the witnesses entered the court, until finally it was my turn. I went into the witness box, swore the oath with the Bible in my hand and faced my inquisitor.

(Funnily enough, I know it was a Bible, because some months previously we had been checking the courtroom and the small bible case fell from its resting place. The book which slid out of the leather case hit the floor, and on picking it up, my sergeant let out an oath which would have made a sailor blush. I looked at the small tome, which read *Old Moore's Almanac, circa 1898*. For years, people had been tried and sentenced on evidence sworn on Old Moore! So a proper Bible was found, and quickly. I've often wondered how the Law would view all the thousands of cases proved guilty in the past, if it had known about this minor blunder!)

My cross-examination began after I had given evidence. I knew that I was in for a rough ride when my pocket book was requested for examination. It was scrutinized by the defence counsel, and the allegation made that I had made up a completely new book for the occasion. This, of course, was ridiculous. I was also able to produce my current pocket book as a comparison. (Neatness of hand is sometimes a drawback!) Questions were asked regarding distances driven at the time of the offence, which truthfully I answered that I had not seen indicated by the milometer.

Counsel drew himself up and, glaring at the bench, with his hand holding his gown lapel, stated;

'I bring Your Worship's attention to R. V. Spuginshaw 1923, where distance was a criterion in evidence. It was ruled that if the officer did not know or could not ascertain the distance travelled, it would be held invalid.'

The chairman, sagely nodding, turned to me.

'Officer. How far did you follow the defendant?'

'I don't know, sir. I didn't have time to note the

reading on the milometer. All I do know is that from the end of the roadworks to the point where we lost sight of the defendant's car was four miles. That is from local knowledge, sir.'

'Thank you, officer. I prefer an "I don't know", to a lot of waffle. Proceed with your questioning, Mr Splutmussel.'

'Thank you, your Worship,' a deferential nod to the bench, and then, 'Constable, you state that my client's speed was in excess of eighty miles per hour? How do you know this?'

'Because I checked the speedometer as we were trying to catch him, sir.'

'And how fast were you travelling at this time?'

'At an indicated eighty miles per hour, sir.'

'Would it surprise you to know that after your obstruction of my client, and his enforced actions to avoid a collision with you as you braked to slow him down, that he was only travelling at fifty miles per hour?'

'It would indeed, sir. And I resent the allegation that your client was obstructed by me.'

'You deny the allegation, officer?' The half-rimmed glasses were removed and the support on one side placed pensively in the mouth.

'I do, sir.'

'What time did you first see my client, officer?'

'I noticed his actions at 3.12 P.M., sir.'

'My client will state, your Worship, that it was nearer 3 P.M. Now officer, what time was my client stopped by a patrol?'

'I believe it was 3.15 P.M., sir. Three minutes after I first noticed his driving.'

'Surely it was closer to 3.05 P.M. when you first saw my client, which meant he travelled five miles in ten minutes. A speed of just about thirty miles an hour, or slightly more allowing for your holding him up.'

I saw the chairman rapidly doing calculations on his

pad, and then; 'Mr Splutmussel. If your client was travelling at just over thirty miles an hour, and the officer states he was travelling at eighty miles an hour to catch your client, then I calculate that the officer would have caught your client after two point six miles.' He smiled benignly down at the QC.

Counsel faltered, and then stated, 'I am no mathematician, your Worship.'

'Well I am, sir,' the chairman stated, 'with a BSc Honours degree. I think you would be advised to change this line of questioning for your client's sake.' The smile was seraphic.

Counsel was rattled. So, when all else fails, destroy the integrity of the policeman.

'Officer. You did not see the milometer. You did not know how far my client had travelled. You do not know what time he was stopped. I put it to you that with all these "don't knows", you are not telling the truth to the court. You are, in fact, lying to this court.' He leaned forward eagerly.

I opened my mouth to reply.

'Mr Splutmussel!' the chairman's voice rang out before I could reply. 'I have known Constable Woodhead for over ten years. His honesty and integrity are beyond reproach, his word is sacrosanct in this court as being the truth. How dare you accuse him of perjury. I will not advise you again regarding the interests of your client, nor your attempts to degrade this officer before this court.'

The counsel turned to face the bench. You could almost see his mind working. Who was this jumped-up little grocer, giving him advice?

'With respect, your Worship, I believe advice should be directed through the learned clerk,' he bowed towards the local solicitor acting in this capacity. His rebuke to the bench delivered, he turned to continue his assault on my good character.

'Mr Splutmussel! Do not antagonize this bench! I was called to the bar in 1958, defended in the criminal central court for four years with a high degree of success before turning to teaching. Now do you question my ability to advise this court?!' The voice thundered, and the QC wilted under its blast. His head bobbed in time with his Adam's apple.

'As your Worship pleases,' he croaked. 'May I ask for an adjournment to consult with my client?'

'An admirable suggestion, sir,' the chairman's voice was silky smooth, and he rose to leave. 'We shall adjourn for ten minutes.'

Twenty minutes later, the court re-sat, and a plea of guilty to careless driving, a lesser charge, was offered and accepted by police prosecution.

On this admission, it was then a case of finding out whether the defendant had any previous convictions. There were reams of them, from courts all over the country. Careless driving, speeding, driving without consideration. The man should have been banned years before, and probably would have been had it not been for his roving brief. Instead, a plea for clemency was eloquently put forward by the now chastened counsel, mitigating his client and begging for the court to resist the sentence of loss of licence. The man was a consultant computer analyst, whose job and the welfare of his wife and three children depended on his ability to drive.

The bench listened patiently, then adjourned again to decide.

On their return, the chairman looked down at both the QC and his luckless client, now obviously worried.

'In accord with your plea for clemency, Mr Splutmussel, we shall not ban your client from driving. However, we have consulted the learned clerk and find that we can impose a fine. So, your client now has three more points against him, and a proviso that should he come before a court again within the next two years, he will be banned for three years. The fine will be a thousand pounds.' He sat back with a satisfied look on his face. The QC sat down with a thump, and his client turned green.

Now *that* was justice!!

21

Lightning Strikes Twice

I was on my meal break one Wednesday evening, having spent four hours battling against the wind and rain. This in itself was unusual, as bad weather had not been forecast, and had resulted in three trees down which had to be cleared from the roads. The major roads were flooding, due to the drains and dykes being unable to cope with the sudden downpour, and this had resulted in a spate of minor road accidents. My paperwork was mounting faster than I could record it in my book. I was tucking into one of my wife's fantastic tuna fish pies, and scribbling furiously into my pocket book balanced precariously on my knee, when the telephone rang. I answered it with resignation in my voice, to be told that a high tension cable was down on one of the major roads, and could I go and investigate.

I telephoned Malc, my opposite number on the adjoining beat, and arranged to meet him at the location. Experience had taught us that two officers were always needed at an incident of this type, and he and I worked well as a team.

Arriving at the scene, I was greeted by a firework display which would have done justice to Messrs Brock & Co. Blue flashes lit the night sky, as the sharply tilted power line poles swayed in the rising wind, their lines snaking and touching in an explosive eruption of arcing electricity. The street lamps, of course, were all out, as were the domestic lights in all the houses. Lying on the road, and curling with snake-like menace was the downed cable. For some reason, it was still very much 'alive', due to the power-carrying cables swinging against it and thereby shorting to earth. Every so often, the frayed end would spit and fizz its blue contents into the wet road. That was bad enough, but to my horror I saw that it lay with almost casual drape over a very expensive, and still inhabited, Vauxhall motor car!

The driver, his eyes the shape and size of a boxer dog's balls, stared out at me with a haunted look. How long he had been in that predicament I have no idea, but the four-way flashes on the car were almost extinguished with the effort of warning approaching traffic. I approached the car with not a little caution, armed with my long-handled wooden broom kept in the minivan for purposes of sweeping glass off the roads after accidents. The driver stared even more intently at me.

'Have you out in a minute, driver,' I called confidently, and he nodded vigorously at my voice.

'I've been in here over an hour,' he called through the tightly shut window. I grinned and nodded sympathetically, relieved to see Malc's blue light approaching at speed.

Then I saw the crowd. In Malc's headlights they stood, in silent silhouette, lining the road for yards on either side. Watching. Waiting with apparently morbid anticipation to see who would get frizzled first. Malc approached, armed with his broom, and like a pair of capped road sweepers, we began the delicate operation of pushing the hissing cable off the roof of the car and on to the road.

Everything went well at first, as with a crackle and spit of annoyance, the cable slid off the roof and bonnet. Then it caught on the wing mirror, and jammed behind the rear bumper. I reversed my broom, and lifted the wire off the mirror, only to see the cable slide with gathering speed down the shaft towards my hands. I dropped the broom with a yelp! Another cacophony of crackles and sparks lit the scene at this move, and the driver of the Vauxhall disappeared beneath the dashboard. The 'oohs' and 'aahs' of the crowd emphasized my close call.

Malc, with great aplomb, had managed to get the trapped cable out of the rear bumper, and came to my aid. Gingerly sliding my scorched broom from under the cable, we tried to lift the cable off the wing mirror. It was at this point we saw the fish and chip van pull up.

Driven by a young lad of great enterprise, it sounded its horn to announce its arrival and, as if by magic, the crowd, plus those who had stayed indoors, made their way chattering along the footpath towards its succulent smell and urgent call.

Having had a bleak time in the town, the young lad had decided to follow the dwindling populace towards the place of excitement. He parked on the road under a severely leaning electricity pole and, lit by the sparks above his vehicle, began to dispense his wares to an ever-growing queue! Malc and I watched with increasing horror as the crowd stepped lightly over twitching cables and meandered through blue sparks falling to the wet pavements. The sudden blackout had obviously interrupted a fancy-dress party somewhere in the road, as a gorilla nodded in friendly greeting to us, followed by two fairies, a witch and Dick Whittington. Standing as we were, with a rogue cable fizzing between two blackened broom handles, and committed to the task in hand, we could only shout at them to get back.

Finally we got the cable off the car, and managed to coil it out of the way. The Vauxhall door opened, and the driver leaped out, glancing over his shoulder as he scampered away from his erstwhile tomb.

'Funny thing about being at death's door,' he stated through tight lips. 'I've got a hell of an appetite.' And to our combined amazement he went over to the chippie for a cod and chips twice. The crowd parted at his approach, appreciating his dilemma, and even gave him a round of applause.

Malcolm and I strode purposefully over to the van, and I gave the young and enterprising man a damned good dressing down.

'MOVE ON,' I ordered, and the crowd around began to shout defiance. It was like a scene from Dante's *Inferno*, flashes and sparks flying from all directions overhead, and a mutinous crowd swelling around us.

'I suppose you've had your tea,' an irate lady shouted at me, 'probably sitting there while this poor man was trapped!' She looked around her and added, 'Lazy sods!'

The crowd nodded and murmured agreement.

A loud crack above us silenced my reply, and we all skittered away from the tumbling sparks. The final explosion seemed to do the trick as far as the power lines were concerned, and those lights left burning in houses further up the road all went out together. As this eliminated the immediate danger to the public, Malc whispered in my ear that the chippie may as well stay where he was. In fact, he could just do with a scampi and chips himself! I sighed, and made my way back to my van to radio for the Electricity Board to attend.

Clutching his bag of supper, Malc followed, dipping into the contents and discussing the evening's events with the gorilla and a witch dressed in a very revealing outfit. Suddenly, they stopped and listened. Then Malc shot up a driveway and into a neat bungalow.

I had arranged for the Electricity Board to get there as soon as possible, and managed to get the Vauxhall bump started and driven off the road when Malc returned to the scene, his eyes streaming with tears and shoulders shaking.

Amidst all the chaos, it appeared that the little old man living in the bungalow had settled himself down for the night in bed. Suddenly, his small bedside light had gone out. He hadn't seen it happen, as he had closed his eyes to try and relax. When he opened his eyes – complete darkness! He thought he had died! Seriously. So he lay there calling 'Help', mainly to try and reassure himself that there was life after death. You can imagine his relief when Malc, who had heard his faint calls, appeared in his bedroom holding a torch. His reactions were slightly more verbal when Malc was followed by a beautiful female dressed in white flowing robes and a gorilla! Hence Malc's hysterical laughter.

With the arrival of the Electricity Board, order was restored quite quickly. Street lights blazed in orange splendour, house lights came on everywhere, the music started up at the fancy-dress party; and we noted that a faint glow was coming from the bedroom window in the bungalow, assuring the little man that he was still alive and kicking. The chippie drove off, much satisfied with his takings, and Malc and I stood with our backs to our vans, quietly lighting our pipes.

All of this was written off in a few lines in our report. 'Attended scene. Cables removed from trapped vehicle and secured. NEEB attended and power restored. Road clear at 23.30 hrs. No further police action.' That was what had happened, everything else was incidental!

22

Right in it!

Road traffic accidents are rarely, if ever, funny. But occasionally, just occasionally, you come across one which has you biting your lip and talking in strangulated tones, accompanied by bouts of coughing.

Such was one I had to deal with some years ago when, due to lack of manpower, I was covering a neighbouring beat as well as my own. The other beat had a large section of the Great North Road running through it, so it was quite a pleasure to cruise down the dual carriageways in my police minivan, and watch the traffic pile up slowly behind me, fearing to overtake. Motorists are strange creatures. Show them a police sign, and they immediately slow down, even if it's attached to a beaten-up little blue minivan travelling at fifty miles an hour. Those who do pluck up courage and swish past, invariably spend the next five minutes watching their rear-view mirrors with haunted eyes, fearing that the blue light will come on. As most of them were in large, very fast cars and I was in the aforesaid clapped-out BMC boneshaker, it is most unlikely that had I *wanted* to stop them, I would ever have caught them! Not that the minivans were that slow. Indeed, some could travel quite fast. Not mine though. I remember being chased by a racing cyclist once, who was using my van as a 'pacer' and I'm sure he would have overtaken me if his chain hadn't broken! However, back to the accident.

I was cruising along, when the sanctity of the moment

was broken by my radio. I answered the call and was informed that further down the A1, a red Renault 5 had been seen to skid violently and leave the road. A traffic car was en route, and the ambulance notified to stand by. Did I know the location as described? I stated that I knew it well. So, on went the blue light, and the traffic behind shrank back in fear.

I arrived at the scene, as described by control, and pulled into the hard shoulder. Sure enough, there in front of me were the signs of a car leaving the road. That is, the signs. Skid marks, swerving wildly about the hard shoulder, across the verge and then disappearing. A bit further on there were signs of wheels leaving the hard shoulder and re-entering the tarmac surface of the A1. The large hedge which bordered the roadside showed no signs of impact at all, standing stiff and straight in all its blackthorn glory.

I returned to the steaming minivan, just as the traffic car stormed up to the scene in a flurry of blue light and two-toned importance. The driver stepped carefully out and raised a quizzical eyebrow. Funny things, traffic men. I suppose it must be the superior cars they drive, and their self assurance determined by reclining seats and twin speed heaters, but they always make me feel not only scruffy, but quite inadequate. Bright yellow 'day-glo' jackets over immaculate uniforms, topped off by white caps. Whereas I stand there, hatless (you can't wear a helmet in a minivan), probably just come from a muddy farm somewhere, having waded through fields of dead broccoli and cow pats, shoes caked in whatever and my trouser knees baggy from sitting in the foetal position required to squeeze six foot of copper into a vehicle built for someone a foot shorter. Anyway, even the raised eyebrow held qualities of superiority. I shrugged, and cringed as the wind whipped at my thinning hair, causing the long wispy bits I use to cover my ever-heightening forehead to fly back and expose my baldness.

'No accident, then?' The traffic man used a tone of voice usually directed at a very small boy who's wet his pants. I shook my head, ashamed at the fact that I didn't have something really twisted and gory to give him. He gazed past me, and casually reached in for his handset.

'Tango nina nina fife,' he intoned in that laid-back manner they have. It's so sickening; if I try to imitate it, I'm always told to repeat my message because no one understands me. Anyway, he was half way through informing control that he had attended the scene and it was all clear, when an apparition was seen wandering slowly up the hard shoulder towards us. It was male, slightly built, and dripping from head to toe with wet, shiny brown stuff that smelled *awful*! Even I felt neat and tidy!

'I've had an accident,' the dripping figure stated in a shaky voice.

'A very frightening one, judging by your appearance,' the traffic man stated laconically, his nose wrinkling in distaste.

The figure nodded pathetically under the immaculate gaze. I began to sympathize.

'Whereabouts, sir?' I enquired, fighting down the urge to pat his arm with a reassuring gesture.

'Over there,' an arm swept to his right, indicating over the high hedge and sending droplets of nasty stuff scattering in an arc. The traffic man jumped backwards behind me, casting concerned looks at his Granada's paintwork. He needn't have worried, I received all there was to receive.

We walked cautiously towards the hedge and, for the first time, I noted that here and there under the hedge and near the root level, there were definite signs of some damage. The pathetic figure pushed at the hedge and, like something from the *Arabian Nights* – the Ali

Baba version – there was a large gap in the hedge, hidden by the fact that the length of the hedge had sheared off at ground level, allowed the car to pass through, and then sprung back to fit exactly in place. A very resilient shrub, the blackthorn.

The ground on the other side of the hedge dipped sharply below road level, dropping away towards a small stream and, prior to that, a large, very full cesspool. It was one that took not only the domestic waste from the farm, but also all the scrapings and shovellings of the cattle byre, pig pens and other sources of highly smelly stuff. Mixed liberally with water, it was then taken away in tanks and spread lustily about the fields and grazings. It was very full. Undoubtably due to that Greek chap's theory about liquid displacing the volume of the object immersed into it. In this case, the object was a red Renault 5, right in the middle, dead centre, awash to just below the windows. It really says something for the door seals on the Renault 5! Sitting in the rear passenger seat, busily knitting, was a lady of quite large proportions apparently oblivious to what had happened to her and her spouse.

'The wife,' the quietly drying and caking little man stated unnecessarily. Then: 'Knitting. She always knits when things get a bit tense.' He smiled weakly at the traffic man, his brown countenance flaking with the effort. Hastily watching the falling particles, lest his sewn-in creases be sullied, the traffic man stated the obvious: 'I would say that in that predicament, things must look a little tense.' He nodded to the faintly bobbing Renault, as the large lady flipped over her pattern page. The little man nodded vigorously, and more of his facepack disappeared in a cloud of dust.

'Er, what happened sir?' I was curious to know.

'Well, we were just driving along, when I thought I had hit a rabbit or something. Anyway, I pulled off the road a bit sharpish, and the next thing I knew the car was snaking about.' He indicated the severity of the car's actions with flailing arms, but subsided under the haughty gaze of the traffic man as his immaculate shirt received a small speckle of gunge.

'Go on,' the traffic lad stated in a tired sort of voice as he dabbed with a spotless white handkerchief at the ruined shirt. The little man continued with downcast eyes and hands clasped wetly together to restrict any further desecration of police equipment.

'Well, we hit the hedge, and shot through it like it wasn't there. Then there was a loud splosh, well, more like a gloop really,' he looked up at me for some encouragement. Having stood in enough of the same, I thought 'gloop' summed it up quite well, and nodded for him to continue.

'That's it, really. When all the, er, the er, stuff subsided we were right in the middle of it.'

'Right in it,' the traffic lad agreed, nodding.

'Then the wife takes out her knitting, and says, "Norman, you'd better go for help!" So I did. I climbed out of the side window, making sure I didn't cause any ripples; we've got new seat covers and carpets in, you know.' He looked at the traffic man proudly and, encouraged by the raised eyebrow, went on, 'And then I did a silly thing,' he paused, then, 'I tried to jump for the side.' He looked down at himself, covered in dried 'gloop', and shook his head sadly. 'It didn't work. I fell in. So I waded to the edge and climbed out. I went up to the hedge, and a car had stopped on the other side. I couldn't see where we had come through at first, so I called out. A man on the other side asked if we were alright, and I told him we had landed in a cesspool. He just laughed. I could hear him laughing as he drove away. Anyway, I had to follow the hedge along until I came to a gate. That's when I saw you and that's it,' he shrugged, and I noticed with some satisfaction that some more speckles landed on the back of the traffic man's shirt, of which he was unaware.

At this point, the farmer turned up. He summed up the situation at a glance and, grinning at the little man, turned on a large tap situated at the bottom of the cesspool. A brown torrent thundered and spluttered its way across the field, to run away down a concrete culvert. The Renault lowered majestically down into the tank, the large lady knitting, apparently quite happy with the situation.

Once the tank was relatively empty, the farmer climbed over the rim and, with great care, lifted the large lady out of the back seat in his muscular arms, to carry her with dignity to the rim and place her gracefully on the grass above the runaway 'gloop'. I think it was the highlight of her day. With such a small husband, I doubted if she had ever been lifted and carried.

The car was a problem that only a large crane could solve, so the traffic man went back to his Granada to organize the job. And close the windows. And wipe off any random specks. Me? I went with the odd couple to the farm house, where the farmer's wife, constantly battling with the effects of brown smelly stuff on clothing, washed, fed and clothed them until their car was safely out. Then I started to giggle, then laugh, and was completely hysterical by the time the traffic man came back.

'What's up with you?' he countered, apparently seeing nothing funny in the whole incident. He looked round the room for support. I shrieked!

'You've got shit on your shirt back!' I howled. He's never forgiven me!

23

The Fur Flies

Get two or more bobbies together in a room, give them a cup of tea, and you have the makings of an entertaining half hour or so. The anecdotes seem to flow, either as a form of information, cons they have arrested in the past, or as a source of light-hearted amusement. Funnily enough, many of the stories are directed against themselves. Especially those involving fights.

By the very nature of the job, violence plays a part in a copper's life. Who else in their right mind would wade into a full-blown punch-up when they could quite easily cross the road or turn round and walk away? Only a fool or a copper.

Then the job itself is becoming more violent. Personally, I put it down to improved communications. In the 'good old days', when bobbies were bound to fixed beats and telephone points, a fight in a pub could be over and done with before he actually got to hear of it. If, on the other hand, he was informed of such a fracas, unless it was within half a mile of him, it was going to take him twenty minutes to walk the distance. By then the trouble would undoubtedly be left to the two fittest and they would be on their last legs.

I remember as a young bobbie being with an older, and very much wiser, officer, who walked at the regulation one mile an hour with feet at 'ten to two' and hands behind his back. On being informed of a fight, we made our way at this sedate and easy pace because, as he ated, slowly, 'A copper doesn't run, laddie. It upsets the public. It also means you're out of breath when you get there, which is no bloody good. Then there's the chance that your arriving on the scene too quickly could mean that the fighters have just got their second wind. So your predicament is then that of being on your own, out of breath, one against two, and their dander is already up and the first blow has been struck, which means they have crossed the line between reason and violence. No, son, you walk nice and steady. That way you have time to prepare yourself and let some back-up get moving towards you. Never leave yourself out on a limb.'

My word, what sound thinking. But in this modern day and age, it no longer holds good. The radio tells you where the trouble is, you're either mobile or are picked up en route, and you arrive as the fight is at its zenith. Hardly surprising that so many young bobbies are injured or assaulted on duty.

I recall a grand fight I was involved in at a holiday resort one year. The main source of our troubles arrived in the form of a tartan army during the first two weeks of August. 'Scots Fortnight' it was called. All the Jocks from Glasgow used to descend on the town, and for fourteen days it was bedlam. Every night was Saturday night!

We were called to a local night club by one of the remaining bouncers (it had been a heavy session for them, and they only called us when they were running out of steam), so five of us and a sergeant turned up in an assortment of vehicles. In the foyer of the club, we were met by the sight of the last remaining bouncer and the manager back to back and fighting like hell with a huge mass of Scots. We piled in and the Jocks wavered a bit, enough to give the bouncer a breather. Then they were back on us again. Funnily enough, while there was punching and slogging there was none of the kicking

183

and head-butting which one associates with the Glas
wegian. Just good, honest (?) down to earth battling witl
fists, with the losers, police or Jocks, being chucked ou
of the front door by the winner, who then ploughe
back into the fray.

Our sergeant was an elderly man, who had undergone
a hernia operation some months previously but he stil
did his bit. Then a shrill blast on a whistle rent the air
and everything stopped. Fists held in mid-flight and
hands round throats relaxed at the sound. Everyone
looked round. The sergeant, his whistle still in hi
mouth, was leaning weakly against a wall.

'It's no good, lads,' he gasped, his whistle dangling
down on his chest. 'That op's just about buggered me.
You'll have to carry on without me.'

The next thing, he was being escorted out of the foyer
by a copper on one arm, and a worried-looking Jock on
the other, and a third Jock opening the door for him. All
faces showed concern for his well-being as he disappeared through the doors.

'Is he going to be alright?' a large Jock, who a few
minutes previously was trying to bust my face open,
asked in a worried voice.

'Yeah,' I nodded, letting my fingers loose from his
hair to rest on his shoulder. 'He's had a hernia operation
recently. Left him a bit weak, that's all.'

'Aye,' the Jock intoned, 'm' faither had 'un last yeer,
y'ken. Bluidy awfu' it wus.'

The two escorts returned, and the doors swung
closed. Then it all started up again! We won, but only
just, thanks to the cavalry turning up, at which point the
Jocks capitulated.

I met them the next afternoon, while I was pounding
my beat along the quayside. They were singing and
laughing, swigging their beer straight out of six-packs
and generally enjoying their holiday. On seeing me,
they came straight over, and I was twitching my hand

towards the radio to shout for help or a Christian burial. But all they wanted to know was whether the sergeant was alright. Then to give me congratulations on behalf of all the Jocks for a 'grrand feit', and that there were no hard feelings. I shook hands with about thirty of them, and promised to meet even more for a drink if I ever got up to Glasgow. Funny thing was, although I had been thumped many times during the evening's dust-up, I didn't have a mark on me. They, on the other hand, were a classic advert for Elastoplast!

As I said before, most of the anecdotes are directed against the teller, and the greater the daftness of their actions, usually the better the story. I've mentioned on previous occasions my opposite number Malc, and it is his turn to come under the spotlight for unintentional idiocy in front of the public.

He had called into his police house for a cuppa while patrolling his beat, intending to clear up some outstanding paperwork. He'd no sooner stopped his minivan in the drive when his very large tom cat leaped up on to the bonnet, to curl up against the warm metal. Malc took a swipe at him with his hat, but the moggie took no apparent notice. Malc went into the house.

Sitting in his office later, the typewriter beginning to glow with the turnout of paperwork, the telephone rang, and Malc was informed that he was to get to the section office 'immediately', to see the Chief Superintendent.

Casting his typing to the wind, he dashed from the house and leaped into the minivan. Out on to the road he drove, his mind racing and his guts clutched in the grip of a cold hand. He knew he hadn't done anything wrong, but nevertheless, he didn't like the idea of an unannounced summons to the royal presence. He waved in half-hearted fashion at the school crossing lady as she flapped her hands at him. He waved again at some school children who recognized his van. He began to feel distinctly popular when two motorists he didn't really recognize flashed their lights and waved. All the way to the station, he was smiling and waving at people who grinned and lifted arms in recognition. Why worry about the bloody Chief Superintendent when all his parishioners knew and loved him.

Feeling quite relaxed and worry free, Malc swung into the yard, where he was confronted by the Chief getting out of his own car. Pulling to a halt, Malc knew he had nothing to panic about, when the Chief's face split into a huge grin of recognition and friendship.

Smiling broadly, Malc got out of his cramped van, and threw up a salute. Then he noticed that the Chief's eyes were not actually on his face, but looking past his right shoulder towards the van roof. The grin slowly fading, Malc turned round and there, curled up in a terrified ball around the blue light, looking like some ghastly Davy Crockett hat, was his large tom cat! Asleep on the roof of the van when Malc had turned out, it had been rudely awakened as its place of rest sped off down the road, and had no alternative but to cling on with tooth and claw. No wonder people had been laughing and waving!

He gave the cat a sickly grin then looked back at the Chief. Then, with hands thrust deep in pockets, he walked dejectedly towards the office.

24

Comeuppance

During my time in the police force I have often been in the position to witness pompous people, myself included, being reduced by public ridicule. An over-inflated ego can be so easily punctured when least expected. My final chapter is devoted to the 'comeuppance' which we all experience at some time in our lives.

For my own part, I know that I was a right 'pain in the arse' to my parishioners when I was first posted to their community. A force to be reckoned with. Someone who descended on the populace with the wrath of God for failing to conform to the million and one laws, acts and by-laws we have to bow to during our daily lives. Such was my reputation, that my appearance in the market place resulted in women abandoning babies in supermarkets, shoppers peering out of plate glass windows in panic, and a Le Mans type sprint from all concerned to get their cars parked straight. I was really a terror! Until that fateful day (for me) when I received my metaphoric kick up the bum in full view of a gloating public.

I had a tendency to 'bellow' at wrong-doers from across the width of the road, which caused them acute embarrassment, and drew attention to my slashed peak and bulled boots as I stood ramrod straight in full view of the public.

On this particular occasion, I watched in amazement as a lady parked her car right across two parked cars, thus blocking them in. She was delivering eggs to a shop, and only wished to stop a few minutes. But to me, she was openly flaunting my authority. So I bellowed at her.

Covered in confusion and embarrassment, she red-facedly moved her car a few yards further on under the sympathetic gaze of the crowded shoppers. Unfortunately, she did exactly the same thing further down the road. This time, she got my full blast even before she got her door opened. In tears almost she drove in kangaroo leapfrogging motion away from the scene.

I folded my arms in a superior fashion, grinning at the world from under my military-style peaked hat, and cast a glance around to see who was staring at me. It was at this stage I felt the warm trickling down the back of my legs. So engrossed had I been in dispensing instant justice and inflating my own ego, I had been totally unaware of a mangy stray labrador which had cocked its leg up against mine during my fusillade of superior verbal harassment. Not so the gloating public! Every steaming droplet had been witnessed, and they gleefully watched my face as I realized what had happened. Mustering my dwindling self respect, I walked with as much dignity as could be summoned down the High Street, endeavouring not to shake the soaking serge as I did so! A most sobering experience, and one which I still have thrown at me across the bar in my local whenever I get a bit 'above myself'.

'Last time you spoke like that, Mr Woodhead, old Arnie's black lab showed his disapproval by peeing up your legs!' And this is fifteen years on!

By the same token, I am human enough to take a slightly sadistic pleasure in the downfall of those in authority. Which brings to mind an incident which occurred many years ago, when Inspectors were a law unto themselves. The intermediate ranks of Chief Inspector and Chief Superintendent did not exist in those days, so the Inspector of Police was someone of great importance.

Some of these men did tend to give themselves airs and graces to which they were not entitled.

One such man was prone to taking the County car out on a Sunday morning to meet a lady of his acquaintance, and together they would burn up County petrol in their meanderings through wooded countryside before putting the ample back seats to a more amorous use. Everyone knew about it at the nick, but such was the man's power, nothing was done or said. Until the complaints began to come in. Usually from the same man, who reported a couple who were 'doing it' in the car park under his window.

'They're at it again,' he would bellow, 'I can see them from here. Right under my window! What's more, my kids can see them as well, and are beginning to ask some awkward questions. I want you to do something about it.'

Unfortunately, the view from his window was such that all the naked writhings on the back seat could be seen, but not the registration number of the car.

So off the sergeant and the duty bobby would pedal on their bikes, to arrive at the little picnic park just as the Inspector drove away, his lady friend still lying flat on the back seat out of sight. Most frustrating. Especially when they both received a bollocking from the Inspector on their return later that morning.

The following week it was the same.

'They're at it again!' the irate man shouted down the phone. 'The dirty sod's all over her. Disgusting, it is. My kids are asking questions about things even I didn't know about. Get over here and do something about it.'

And so it went on. Until one day the sergeant and the duty bobby left the station early, giving the office man a call box number to ring as soon as the complaint was received.

Sure enough, later that morning, he was on again, 'They're here again! I don't know where he gets his stamina from, I really don't! Banging away under my window, like sex is going to be taxed in the next ten minutes! I'm fed up with it! Now the wife's making comparisons, and I've got a hernia to compete with. For Pete's sake get it stopped!'

The office man, fingers trembling with excitement, dialled the call box number, and the sergeant with his cohort set off on silent tyres in response to its ring. It was a very surprised and naked inspector who looked up at the side window in reply to the sergeant's knocking with truncheon. The lady, on the other hand, went rigid with shock. Legs locked together in a vice-like grip under the Inspector, trapped him in a painful and delicate place with thigh muscles that rippled in powerful panic. Clamped tightly to his ladylove, the Inspector looked up with a haunted expression. The bobby walked around the car, taking note of the number, time and date and, when all was duly recorded, he called the complainant down to witness the event.

Oh, how they enjoyed it. To extract the Inspector a bucket of water was thrown over the woman, who relaxed fractionally with the shock and allowed the unfortunate man to extricate his damaged bits and pieces from her passionate clamp. Slowly and precisely, the sergeant cautioned them both, and reported them for breach of the peace, as the constable licked his pencil and laboriously recorded everything that was said.

As is usual in these incidents, a senior officer above the rank of Inspector was notified and after a short but heated interview a very dejected man limped out of the room and left the station. An early retirement followed afterwards. Ah, how the mighty are fallen. Now this happened quite a few years ago, but there are some who would do well to think seriously on the moral, especially those who think they are fireproof!

Finally, a more modern 'comeuppance' which came to light in a large station in a large city.

There was this solicitor who was always available when any offender was locked up for whatever offence. He would appear with bundles of writs for habeas corpus and the arresting officer would see his prisoner whipped out from under his nose before he had a chance to question him. Most frustrating! The solicitor became almost unbearable in his attitude, puffing himself up with self importance. Now this isn't sour grapes. Every bobby knows that the prisoner is allowed to see his brief and, providing it doesn't 'interfere with the course of justice', will contact the legal representative when requested. But this man appeared almost as soon as his client was banged up!

So it was a very annoyed station sergeant who was called in to see his superintendent after he had had words with the solicitor. The sergeant, exasperated at this man's appearance every time an offender was brought in, had said his piece in no uncertain terms. Now he was in front of the boss, and the terms of the new Police and Criminal Evidence Act were was thrust down his throat. But he need not have worried. 'Come-uppance' was at hand.

That night, a traffic patrol saw a large car drive past them at high speed and in a very erratic manner. Giving chase, they were just in time to see the saloon hit a bollard, bounce off a wall and come to rest crumpled against a large Post Office van. The driver, a youth, was caught before he had scrambled clear. He wasn't hurt, and as it wasn't his car, not particularly bothered.

'I'll be out of here in ten minutes,' he stated cockily, 'and I'm saying nothing until I get my brief.' He then gave the name of the solicitor. The duty sergeant complied, and telephoned the man's house. An hour later, the brief turned up at the nick, red faced and very cross.

'I would have been here sooner, sergeant,' he said, 'but someone has stolen my car.'

And whose car was it, all crumpled and bent! Yup!

So, there it is. A book about the men and women under the helmets and chequered hats. Stories which I enjoyed when I first heard them and have recounted here with great pleasure.

I know that the police do, from time to time, come in for some real flak in the Press and on TV. Some of it is justified, some not. But whatever your own opinions of the 'boys (and girls) in blue', remember one thing, the public gets the police force it deserves, enforcing the law as passed by the constitutionally elected Government. England, Wales and Scotland are still the only places in the world where a single, unarmed man (or woman) is sent to any call received and will deal with it. No visible guns, or staffs or metal-tipped sticks. Just a dark uniform, a helmet and a number clearly visible on the shoulders to enable those that aren't satisfied to complain without fear of reprisal.

Go abroad sometime. Then come back. Alright, you look out for the first familiar signs of Great Britain. The white cliffs? No. Cars being driven on the 'wrong' side of the road? No way!

No. When you see the first Bobby's helmet and that distinctive walk, then you know you're home!